Exploring maths

Home Book

2

PEARSON
Longman

Anita Straker, Tony Fisher, Rosalyn Hyde, Sue Jennings and Jonathan Longstaffe

Published and distributed by Pearson Education Limited, Edinburgh Gate, Harlow, Essex, CM20 2JE, England
www.longman.co.uk

First published 2008

ISBN-13 978-1-405-84409-3

Freelance Development Editor: Sue Glover

Typeset by Tech-Set, Gateshead

Printed and bound in Great Britain at Scotprint, Haddington

The publisher's policy is to use paper manufactured from sustainable forests.

Picture Credits
The publisher would like to thank the following for their kind permission to reproduce their photographs:

(Key: b-bottom; c-centre; l-left; r-right; t-top)

Alamy Images: Simon Belcher 44b; Matt Botwood 28r; Bubbles Photolibrary 54r, 99b; Cephas Picture Library 58r; Tony Cordoza 44t; Heather Gail Delaney 59tl; Robert Fried 25; Leslie Garland Picture Library 58l; Neil Holmes Freelance Digital 116; Chris Howes/Wild Places Photography 73l; ImageState Royalty Free 46; Matthew Jackson 4; Richard Levine 67l, 67r; Melvyn Longhurst 111t; Ian Miles-Flashpoint Pictures 98; Eric Nathan 59b; Richard Naude 9; Photo Network 11t; PhotoStockFile 103; John Rensten 99t; T.M.O.Buildings 117; Hugh Threlfall 73r; Transport of Delight 75; Colin Underhill 11b; Ken Welsh 125; Jim West 64; Westend61 69; **Ardea:** John Mason 43t; **The Art Archive:** National Museum Bucharest/Alfredo Dagli Orti 49; **Corbis:** ImageShop 110; Jennie Woodcock; Reflections Photolibrary 59tc; **DK Images:** Paul Bricknell 16b, 62tl, 62tr; Joe Cornish 54l; Steve Gorton 15, 56l, 60c, 88b, 88t; Jacqui Hurst 6; Dave King 71r; Tracy Morgan 63; Ian O'Leary 60l; Tim Ridley 71l, 80t, 93; Kim Sayer 124; Steve Shott 83; Clive Streeter 73c; Cecile Treal and Jean-Michel Ruiz 95; **Getty Images:** Altrendo Travel 62b; Laurence Dutton/The Image Bank 111b; Euan Myles/Stone 84; Ian O'Leary/Stone 82; Mark Scott/Taxi 43b; Elizabeth Simpson/Taxi 79; Hiroshi Watanabe/Taxi Japan 74b; **iStockphoto:** 3, 38l, 59tr; Galina Barskaya 78, 96; Dennys Bisogno 36; Vera Bogaerts 86l; Nancy Catherine 38c; Andrew Dernie 114; Joanne Green 97; Clayton Hansen 56c; Justin Horrocks 60r; Andrew Johnson 53; Murat Koc 71c; Kathy Konkle 22b; Peter Memmott 80b; Oman Mirzaie 44cr; Nicolette Neish 38r; Sergej Petrakov 37; Ivan Stevanovic 44cl; Linda Steward 86r; Sami Suni 52; Joseph White 56r; **Jupiter Unlimited:** BananaStock 74t; Brand X 102; Creatas Images 94; **Jonathan Longstaffe:** 126; **MB Artists/John Manders:** 50; **Pearson Education Ltd:** 16t; EMG Education Management Group 48; Pearson Learning Photo Studio 62tc; PH College 28c, 28l; Silver Burdett Ginn 17, 18, 19, 20, 21, 22t, 77 (a), 77 (b), 77 (c); **Rex Features:** Andre Seale/SplashdownDirect 12; **SuperStock:** Steve Vidler 45

Cover images: *Front:* **Alamy Images:** Steven Haggard

All other images © Pearson Education

Picture Research by: Louise Edgeworth

Every effort has been made to trace the copyright holders and we apologise in advance for any unintentional omissions. We would be pleased to insert the appropriate acknowledgement in any subsequent edition of this publication.

Contents

Properties of numbers

TASK 1: Square numbers

Points to remember

⊙ A number multiplied by itself is a **square number**.

⊙ A square number can be shown as dots arranged in a square.

⊙ 81 is the square of 9. It can be written as 9^2.

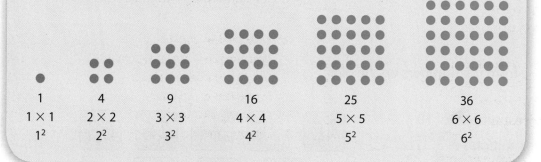

1	4	9	16	25	36
1×1	2×2	3×3	4×4	5×5	6×6
1^2	2^2	3^2	4^2	5^2	6^2

(1) Copy and complete this table.

Numbers	3	6	7		4		11	15	
Squares	9	36		25		81			144

(2) What number goes in each red box?

    a $3^2 + 4^2 = \square^2$ b $6^2 + \square^2 = 10^2$

    c $\square^2 + 12^2 = 15^2$ d $5^2 + \square^2 = 13^2$

(3) You can write 51 as the sum of three square numbers.

    $51 = 49 + 1 + 1$

Write 150 as the sum of three square numbers.
Find three different ways to do it.
Use your calculator to help you.

TASK 2: Multiples and divisibility

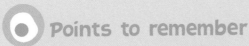

Points to remember

⊙ **Multiples** of 5 are numbers that divide exactly by 5.

⊙ A number is:
- a multiple of **2** if its last digit is even;
- a multiple of **3** if its digit sum is a multiple of 3;
- a multiple of **4** if half of it is even;
- a multiple of **5** if its last digit is 0 or 5;
- a multiple of **10** if its last digit is 0.

① Write down the first three multiples of each of these numbers.

   a 5   b 7   c 8   d 31

② Choose from the numbers on the tiles.
   Write:

   a three multiples of 10
   b five multiples of 5
   c four multiples of 9
   d five multiples of 8
   e three multiples of 6.

   40 75 24 16 63
     60 39 45
   50 32 81 72 22

③ Copy and complete this diagram for the numbers from 30 to 50.

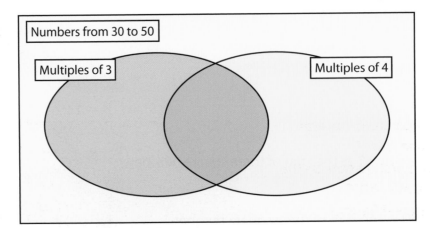

TASK 3: Positive and negative integers

Points to remember

- The negative number −6 is 'negative 6'.
- −10 is less than −5.
- Six degrees below zero is minus six degrees Celsius (−6 °C).
- −10 °C is a lower temperature than −5 °C.
- Always include the units when you write a temperature.

1. At midnight the temperature was −5 °C.
   By 9:00 am the temperature had risen by 3 degrees.
   Find the temperature at 9:00 am.

2. At 6:00 pm the temperature was 4 °C.
   By 11:00 pm the temperature was −5 °C.
   What was the change in temperature between 6:00 pm and 11:00 pm?

3. The map shows four cities and their temperatures at dawn.
   a Put the four temperatures in order.
      Start with the lowest.
   b Work out the difference in temperature between:
      i London and Birmingham
      ii Birmingham and Edinburgh
      iii Edinburgh and London
      iv Birmingham and Bristol

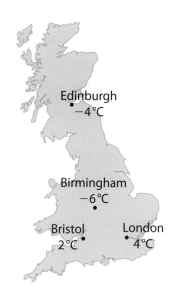

Edinburgh
−4 °C

Birmingham
−6 °C

Bristol
2 °C

London
4 °C

4. The temperature inside an aeroplane is 20 °C.
   The temperature outside the aeroplane is −30 °C.
   What is the difference between these temperatures?

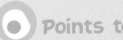

Graphs, charts and tables

TASK 1: Tally charts, bar charts and pictograms

> **◉ Points to remember**
>
> - ⊙ A **tally chart** helps you to sort and count data using tally marks.
> - ⊙ **Bar charts** and **pictograms** are ways of showing data.
> - ⊙ The **frequency** is the total number in each category.

Example

The bar chart and the pictogram below show the same data.
They show the colour of the cars passing a road junction in 20 minutes.

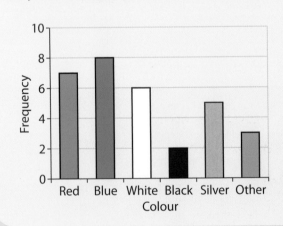

1. This bar chart shows the type of vehicle passing a busy road junction during one day.

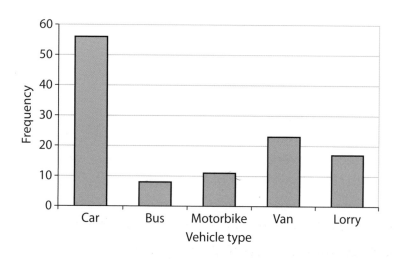

   a What was the most common type of vehicle?

   b What was the least common type of vehicle?

   c How many buses came past?

   d How many more motorbikes than buses came past?

   e Copy and complete this sentence.

   The bar chart shows that the most common type of vehicle was a ....
   and the least common was a ....

2. This pictogram shows the number of people in cars.

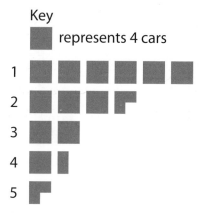

   a What was the most common number of people in a car?

   b What was the least common number of people in a car?

   c How many cars had three people in them?

   d How many cars had two people in them?

TASK 2: Venn and Carroll diagrams

 Points to remember

- Venn and Carroll diagrams are sorting diagrams.
- A Carroll diagram has rectangles.
- A two-way Venn diagram has two overlapping circles:
  - data in the intersection (overlap) has both properties;
  - data outside both circles has neither of the properties.

This **Carroll diagram** shows the ages of some pupils and whether or not some they cycle to school.

There are 7 pupils.

No one aged 13 cycles to school.

	Does not cycle to school	Cycles to school
Aged 13	Asha, Petra, Giselle	
Not aged 13	Amanda, Sam, Clemmy	Freya

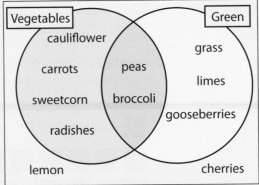

The **Venn diagram** shows whether some plants are vegetables and whether they are green.

The intersection contains the vegetables that are green. Plants that are not vegetables and are not green are outside the circles.

① Copy this Carroll diagram.

	Even	Not even
Multiple of 9	18 90 54	9 81
Not a multiple of 9	16 28	15 29 37

a Write another number in the top left box.

b Write another number in the top right box.

c Write another number in the bottom left box.

d Write another number in the bottom right box.

② Look at this Venn diagram.

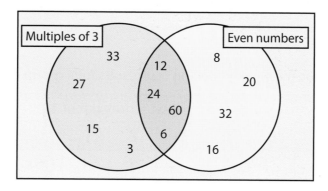

The circle on the right contains even numbers.
The numbers in the left circle are multiples of 3.

a For the blue area, write three more numbers that are multiples of 3.

b For the yellow area, write three more numbers that are even but not multiples of 3.

c For the green area, write two more numbers that are even and are multiples of 3.

TASK 3: Mode and range

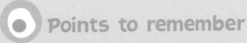

Points to remember

⊙ The **mode** is the most common value in a set of data.

⊙ To find the **range**, subtract the smallest value from the largest.

Example

Jermaine waited for his school bus each morning for two school weeks.
He wrote down the number of minutes he had to wait.

3,   4,   1,   5,   6,   12,   3,   1,   4,   1

a   What is the mode for his waiting time?
The mode of Jermaine's waiting times was 1 minute.
This was his most common waiting time.

b   What is the range of his waiting times?
The range was 12 − 1 = 11 minutes.
This is the difference between the longest and shortest times
he had to wait.

1   The table shows the weekly spelling test results for a group of pupils.

Pupil	Test scores out of 10									
	A	**B**	**C**	**D**	**E**	**F**	**G**	**H**	**I**	**J**
Week 1	4	5	8	7	5	4	6	6	4	4
Week 2	7	8	6	7	8	8	7	6	8	6
Week 3	10	9	6	1	2	4	5	7	3	2
Week 4		10	8	10	9	9	8	9	9	9
Week 5	5	7	6	5	8	4	5	5	6	8

a   For each week, work out the mode and range.

b   Why do you think there is no score for pupil A in week 4?

c   In which week do you think the spelling test was easiest?
Why?

d   In which week do you think the spelling test was hardest?
Why?

Whole numbers

TASK 1: Place value, ordering and rounding

⊙ Points to remember

- ⊙ When you put numbers in order, look at the value of each digit.
- ⊙ < means 'less than' and > means 'more than'.
- ⊙ Round fives up. For example, 425 rounds to 430, and 650 rounds to 700.

(1) Write eighty-eight thousand in figures.

(2) Here is part of a number line.

8000   9000

What number is the red arrow pointing to?

(3) a Round 4632 to the nearest 10.

    b Round 5473 to the nearest 100.

(4) a The mileometer on my car shows 02699 miles.

      i What will it show when it has gone one more mile?

      ii What will it show when it has gone ten more miles?

    b My car cost more than £8600 but less than £9100. Which of these prices could be the cost of the car?

      A £8569   B £9090   C £9130   D £8999

(5) Here are some digit cards.

Use the cards to make three-digit numbers greater than 400.
Write all the numbers that you can make.

TASK 2: Mental addition and subtraction

> ### ● Points to remember
> ⊙ When you add numbers in your head, it is often easier to start with the larger number.
>
> ⊙ Use an empty number line to record or explain your mental methods.

1 Copy and complete the calculations.
Use two of these numbers each time.

17   28   29   37   43

a ... − ... = 8

b ... + ... = 65

c ... + ... = 80

d ... − ... = 11

e ... − ... = 20

f ... − ... = 26

g ... − ... = 9

h ... + ... = 71

i ... + ... = 54

j ... − ... = 15

2 Use the same numbers again.
Make four more calculations.
The answers should be different from any of the answers in question 1.

a ... + ... =

b ... − ... =

c ... + ... =

d ... − ... =

TASK 3: Written methods

Points to remember

- Look at the numbers before you decide how to do a calculation.
- When you use a written method to add or subtract, line up the digits in columns. Write units under units, tens under tens, and so on.

1. Copy and complete this table. Show all your working.

	Calculation	Estimate	Correct answer
a	938 + 426		
b	850 − 261		
c	3159 + 1822		
d	6511 − 4499		

2. Tom collected 439 cans for recycling.
   Joe collected 268 cans.

   a How many cans did they collect altogether?

   b How many more cans did Tom collect than Joe?

3. Pupils at a school collected 28 751 cans for recycling.
   In the following year they collected 8456 more cans.
   How many cans did they collect altogether?

4. Rema went shopping.
   She bought a new laptop for £1239, a printer for £328 and a scanner for £186.
   How much change did she have from £2000?

5.
   8214 people took part in a fun run.
   1765 of them dropped out during the run.
   How many people finished the run?

TASK 4: Problem solving

1. You have to build a shelter on an island.

You need to measure some lengths. You have only these ropes to measure with.

| 6 m | 9 m | 17 m | 19 m | 21 m |

To find a sum, you can put ropes end to end.
To find a difference, you can put ropes side by side.
Which two ropes will measure these distances?

a	11 m	b	27 m	c	3 m
d	28 m	e	10 m	f	4 m
g	8 m	h	26 m	i	13 m

2. Copy this grid.
Use each of the numbers 1 to 9.
Write one number in each box.
Each row, column and diagonal must have a total
that is an **odd number**.

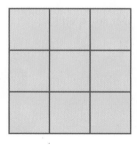

TASK 5: Multiplying and dividing by 10, 100 and 1000

Did you know that...?

Zero is sometimes called **nought**.

Here are some other names for zero. How many of them have you heard of?

aught, cipher, cypher, nada, naught, nil, none, nowt, null, oh, squat, zed, zilch, zip

Points to remember

- When a number is:
    - × **10**, its digits move **1** place to the left;
    - × **100**, its digits move **2** places to the left;
    - × **1000**, its digits move **3** places to the left.

- When a number is:
    - ÷ **10**, its digits move **1** place to the right;
    - ÷ **100**, its digits move **2** places to the right;
    - ÷ **1000**, its digits move **3** places to the right.

1. Which of these have the same value as 7500?
   A 75 hundreds
   B 7500 ones
   C 75 tens
   D 750 tens
   E 750 hundreds

2. How many hundreds are there altogether in 2400?

3. Two of these numbers will multiply together to make 1 million.
   Write the two numbers.

   10   100   1000   10 000   100 000

4. Copy and complete.
   a $9500 \div 10 = \ldots$
   b $10\,000 \div 1000 = \ldots$
   c $51 \times \ldots = 5100$
   d $4600 \times 1000 = \ldots$
   e $54\,000 \div 100 = \ldots$
   f $830 \div \ldots = 83$
   g $100 \times 100 = \ldots$
   h $100\,000 \div 100 = \ldots$

TASK 6: Multiplication tables

 Did you know that...?

The number **2520** is very special.

2520

It is the smallest number that divides exactly by each of 1, 2, 3, 4, 5, 6, 7, 8, 9 or 10.

Points to remember

⊙ 5 times a number is half 10 times the number.
  20 times a number is double 10 times the number.

⊙ 4 times a number is double 2 times the number.
  6 times a number is double 3 times the number.
  8 times a number is double 4 times the number.

⊙ 9 times a number is 10 times the number, minus the number.

⊙ 7 times a number is 5 times the number, plus 2 times the number.

---

① Write the answers.

a 7×20	b 9×70	c 30×8
d 50×4	e 5×800	f 700×4
g 8×900	h 300×9	i 50×60
j 90×60	k 70×70	l 80×50

② Copy this grid.

1	2	4	8
5	3	2	3
7	7	1	6
2	6	3	9

Cross out just two numbers.

Each row and column must have a total that is a multiple of 5.

TASK 7: Multiplication

Points to remember

- Use multiplication facts you know to work out others.
- Using a grid can help you to multiply.
- When you multiply, estimate the answer first.
- Check your answer against the estimate.
- Check that your answer is sensible for the problem.

1. Here are three digit cards.

Arrange them like this to make a multiplication.

What is the greatest product you can make?
Write it in your book.

2. Solve these problems.

a A tin of paint costs £14.
Find the cost of 7 tins of paint.

b A machine fills 9 tins of paint in 1 minute.
How many tins of paint does it fill in
15 minutes?

c Rachel pours lemonade into 5 glasses.
She puts 165 millilitres in each glass.
How much lemonade does Rachel pour out?

d 13 buses are used on a school visit.
Each bus can seat 36 pupils.
How many pupils can go on the visit?

e A packet contains 27 biscuits.
How many biscuits are there in 32 packets?

TASK 8: Division

1 Solve these problems.

   a Faisel buys 7 DVDs.
They are all the same price.
He pays £91.
What is the cost of one DVD?

   b Andrew buys 8 train tickets.
The total cost is £96.
What is the cost of one ticket?

   c Molly buys 5 birthday cards.
They are all the same price.
She gets 5p change from £1.
What is the cost of one birthday card?

2 Do these. Think whether to round your answer up or down.

   a Amrita has 107 small cakes.
She wants to put 4 cakes on each plate.
How many plates does she need?

   b Debbie buys eggs for the corner shop.
She has bought 85 eggs this week.
She packs them in boxes of 6 eggs.
How many boxes of eggs does she fill?

3 27 is a multiple of 3.
When you reverse the digits, 72 is also a multiple of 3.

Write all the multiples of 6 between 10 and 100.
Reverse the digits.
Which of these numbers are also multiples of 6?

Patterns and sequences

TASK 1: Continuing sequences

Points to remember

- A **sequence** of numbers follows a rule.
- Each number in a sequence is a **term**.
- The sequence 1, 3, 5, 7, … is in **ascending** order so it is **increasing**.
- The sequence 50, 47, 44, 41, 38, … is in **descending** order so it is **decreasing**.

1. Write the rule for each sequence.
   Then find the next three terms of each sequence.

   a 5,   7,   9,   11,   13,   …,   …,   …

   b 2,   11,   20,   29,   38,   …,   …,   …

   c 1,   5,   9,   13,   17,   …,   …,   …

   d 3,   8,   13,   18,   23,   …,   …,   …

   e 100,   97,   94,   91,   88,   …,   …,   …

2. Look at this sequence of numbers.

   2,   9,   16,   23,   30,   37,   44,   51,   …

   a What is the 1st term?

   b What is the 4th term?

   c What is the 8th term?

   d What is the difference between the 2nd term and the 3rd term?

   e Write the next three terms of the sequence after 51.

TASK 2: Sequences from rules

⊙ Points to remember

⊙ You can make a sequence if you know the **first term** and the **rule**.
For example, if the first term is 6 and the rule is 'add 4', the sequence is:
6,   10,   14,   18,   22,   26,   …

1 Write the first five terms of each of these sequences.

	1st term	Term-to-term rule
a	2	add 10
b	7	add 8
c	105	subtract 5
d	250	subtract 10

2 Copy and complete each sequence.

a 2,   4,   6,   8,   ☐,   ☐,   14

b ☐,   ☐,   10,   13,   16,   19,   ☐

c 1,   ☐,   ☐,   13,   17,   ☐,   25

d 80,   73,   ☐,   ☐,   52,   45,   ☐

e ☐,   ☐,   12,   ☐,   24,   30,   36

f 15,   ☐,   7,   3,   −1,   ☐,   ☐

TASK 3: Multiples

> ## Points to remember
> - A **multiple** of a number divides exactly by that number.
>   For example, 5, 10, 15, 100, 345, … are multiples of 5 because they divide exactly by 5.

1. a Describe this sequence of numbers.

       3,   6,   9,   12,   15,   18,   21,   24,   …

   b What is the 4th term of the sequence?

   c What is the 7th term of the sequence?

   d What will be the 10th term of the sequence?

   e What is the rule for any term of the sequence?

2. a Describe this sequence of numbers.

       5,   10,   15,   20,   25,   30,   35,   40,   …

   b What is the 3rd term of the sequence?

   c What is the 6th term of the sequence?

   d What will be the 10th term of the sequence?

   e What is the rule for any term of the sequence?

TASK 4: Factors

⦿ Points to remember

⊙ A **factor** of a number divides exactly into that number with no remainder.
For example, the factors of 10 are 1, 2, 5, 10.

⊙ A **prime number** has only two factors, 1 and itself.
For example, 7 is a prime number because it has only two factors, 1 and 7.

1. Write all the factors of each of these numbers.

   a 4   b 9

   c 16   d 11

   e 25   f 21

2. Which of these numbers are prime numbers?

   a 5   b 15

   c 9   d 2

   e 17   f 21

   g 19   h 3

3. Copy the diagram.
   Write each of the numbers 5, 6, 7 and 8 in the correct places on the diagram.

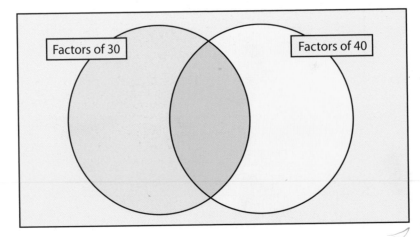

TASK 5: Investigating patterns

Points to remember

- Work out a pattern made by shapes by looking at the way the pattern increases or decreases.
- The number sequence helps you to work out how many shapes you need to make a pattern.
- Finding a rule for working out the number of shapes needed saves time.

①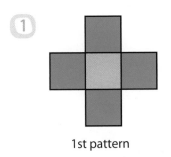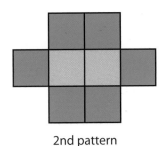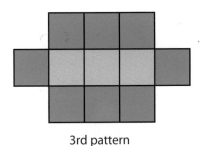

      1st pattern   2nd pattern   3rd pattern

a Write the sequence for the number of pink tiles.

b How many pink tiles will be in the 5th pattern?

c How many pink tiles will be in the 10th pattern?

d Describe how the number of pink tiles increases each time.

e Write the sequence for the number of green tiles.

f How many green tiles will be in the 4th pattern?

g How many green tiles will be in the 18th pattern?

h Describe how the number of green tiles increases each time.

TASK 6: Making general statements

Points to remember

⊙ Use what you know about numbers to describe a number or a sequence.
For example, in the sequence

3, 6, 9, 12, 15, …

each number is a multiple of 3.
The 10th term is 3×10.
The 100th term is 3×100.

1 a What is this number?

Clues

- The number is even.
- The number is less than 20.
- The number is greater than 10.
- 3 is a factor of the number.
- The number is a multiple of 9.

b What is this number?

Clues

- The number is odd.
- The number is less than 50.
- The number is greater than 40.
- The number is not a multiple of 5.
- The number is not a prime number.

2 Describe each sequence.
Write the 10th term.

a 2, 4, 6, 8, 10, …

b 5, 10, 15, 20, 25, …

c 7, 14, 21, 28, 35, …

d 10, 20, 30, 40, 50, …

Fractions, decimals and percentages

TASK 1: Fractions of shapes

> **Points to remember**
>
> ⊙ To shade $\frac{3}{8}$ of a shape, divide it into 8 equal parts and shade 3 of them.

You will need squared paper.

1　What fraction of each shape is coloured?

a 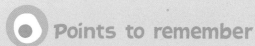　b　c

d 　e 　f

g 　h 　i

2　Draw each rectangle on squared paper. Shade the fraction.

a　Shade $\frac{1}{4}$.

b　Shade $\frac{3}{4}$.

c　Shade $\frac{1}{5}$.

d　Shade $\frac{3}{5}$.

e　Shade $\frac{2}{3}$.

f　Shade $\frac{5}{6}$.

TASK 2: Equivalent fractions

> ## Points to remember
>
> ⊙ To change a fraction to an equivalent fraction, multiply the numerator and the denominator by the same number.
>
> ⊙ To simplify a fraction, divide the numerator and the denominator by the same number. This is called 'cancelling'.

Use these number lines to help you.

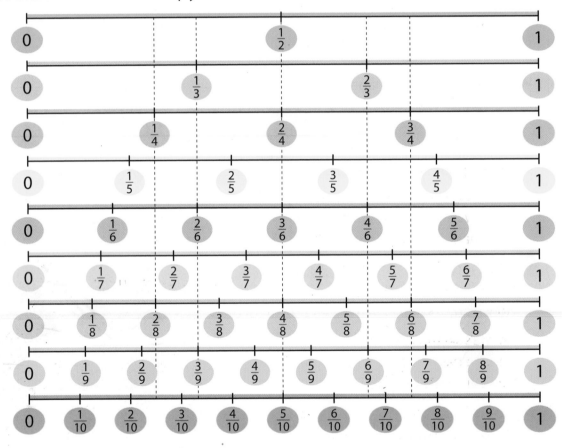

1. a Write four fractions equivalent to $\frac{1}{2}$. b Write two fractions equivalent to $\frac{2}{3}$.

2. a Is $\frac{1}{4}$ bigger or smaller than $\frac{1}{3}$? b Is $\frac{1}{8}$ bigger or smaller than $\frac{1}{9}$?

   c Is $\frac{2}{3}$ bigger or smaller than $\frac{3}{4}$? d Is $\frac{1}{4}$ bigger or smaller than $\frac{1}{3}$?

3. Simplify these fractions.

   a $\frac{8}{10}$ b $\frac{6}{9}$ c $\frac{4}{12}$ d $\frac{15}{25}$

TASK 3: Fractions of quantities

Points to remember

- Find fractions of numbers by dividing.
  For example, to find one tenth, divide by 10.
- To find one quarter, find one half of one half.
- To find three quarters, first find one quarter, then multiply it by 3.
- To find two thirds, first find one third, then multiply it by 2.

1. Work these out. Show your working.

   a $\frac{9}{10}$ of 50   b $\frac{2}{7}$ of 21   c $\frac{3}{4}$ of 32

   d $\frac{3}{10}$ of £150   e $\frac{2}{5}$ of 45 kg   f $\frac{3}{8}$ of 48 m

   g $\frac{2}{3}$ of 18 miles   h $\frac{3}{4}$ of 24 minutes i $\frac{4}{5}$ of 15 days

2. Solve these problems. Show your working.

   a James ate $\frac{5}{8}$ of a bowl of cherries.
     There were 24 cherries in the bowl.
     How many cherries did James eat?

   b A full bottle of milk contains 450 millilitres.
     $\frac{2}{3}$ of the milk has been used.
     How many millilitres of milk have been used?

   c Amrita's ski trip cost £320.
     Her dad paid $\frac{3}{10}$ of the cost.
     How much did he pay?

   d Amrita had dinner with five friends.
     The dinner cost 54 euros altogether.
     Amrita paid $\frac{1}{6}$ of the cost.
     How much did she pay?

TASK 4: Decimal place value

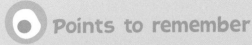

Points to remember

⊙ The decimal point separates the whole number from the decimal fraction.

⊙ Each digit in a decimal number has a value based on its position.

⊙ The first decimal place is for tenths,
   the second decimal place is for hundredths,
   the third decimal place is for thousandths, and so on.

1 Copy and complete these statements.

In 25.39   a the 3 stands for ………   b the 2 stands for ………

c the 9 stands for ………   d the 5 stands for ………

2 What is the value of the 6 in each of these numbers?

a 14.6   b 3.06   c 264.2   d 34.56

3 What number is each arrow pointing to?

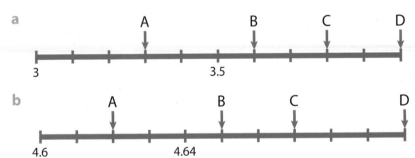

4 Write the next three terms in each sequence.

a 6.2   6.3   6.4   …   …   …

b 4.6   4.7   4.8   …   …   …

c 9.4   9.3   9.2   …   …   …

d 8.62   8.63   8.64   …   …   …

TASK 5: Tenths and hundredths

Points to remember

- 1 whole is equivalent to 10 tenths, or 100 hundredths.
- 1 tenth is equivalent to 10 hundredths.
- 7 tenths is equivalent to 70 hundredths.

1. Write as fractions.

   a 0.3   b 0.07   c 0.23

2. Add up each set of coins. Write the total in **pounds**.

   a

   b

   c

   d

3. Write in centimetres.

   a 2.08 m   b 9.5 m

4. Write in metres.

   a 67 cm   b 420 cm

5. Write in millimetres.

   a 7.2 cm   b 0.3 cm

6. Write in centimetres.

   a 31 mm   b 520 mm

TASK 6: Percentages of quantities

Points to remember

- Per cent means 'in every hundred'. 15% means $\frac{15}{100}$.
- 50% is one half, 25% is one quarter, and 75% is three quarters.
- 10% is one tenth. To find 10% of an amount, divide it by 10.
- To find 60%, first find 10%, then multiply by 6.

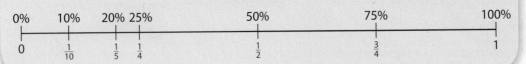

1. What percentage of each shape is shaded?

   a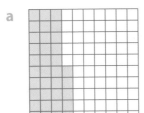

   b

   c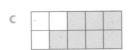

   d

2. 55% of the houses in a street have broadband.
   What percentage of the houses don't have broadband?

3. Work out these percentages.
   - a 10% of £20
   - b 30% of £20
   - c 70% of £50
   - d 20% of 30 kg
   - e 40% of 400 ml
   - f 60% of 200 m

Length, perimeter and area

TASK 1: Length

⊙ Points to remember

⊙ When you use a ruler to measure or draw lines, line up the zero on the ruler with the beginning of the line.

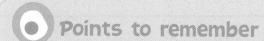

⊙ 1 metre is the same as 100 centimetres.

⊙ 1 centimetre is the same as 10 millimetres.

You will need a ruler and sharp pencil.

1. Gareth uses a ruler marked in centimetres and millimetres to measure some lines. How long is each line?

a

b

2. Estimate the length of each line. Write your estimates in your book.

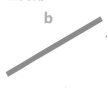

Use a ruler to measure each line accurately.
Write each measurement next to your estimate.

3. Use a ruler and sharp pencil to draw lines with a length of:

   a 6.2 cm   b 46 mm   c 12.8 cm

4 Myoko measured a straight line.
   She said it was 6 cm long.

   Here is a picture of the line she measured
   and where she placed the ruler.

   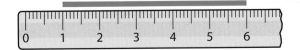

   Do you agree with her answer?
   Explain why.

5 Patrick has drawn a line 136 mm long.
   Helen has drawn a line 16 cm long.

   a Who has drawn the longer line? Explain how you know.

   b What is the difference in the lengths of the two lines?

TASK 2: Perimeter

Points to remember

- The **perimeter** is the total distance around the edge of a shape.
- Perimeters are measured in units of length such as mm, cm or m.
- To find the perimeter of a shape, add the lengths of all the sides.
- A formula for the perimeter of a rectangle is:
  perimeter of a rectangle = (length + width) × 2

1 The grid has 1 cm by 1 cm squares. Work out the perimeter of each shape.

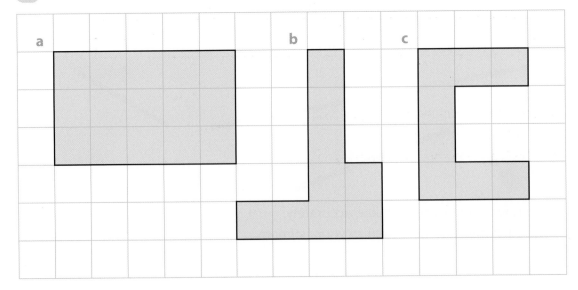

2 Calculate the perimeters of these shapes.
The length of each side is shown.

a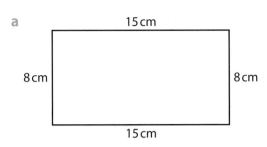

b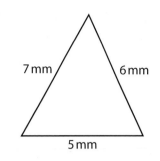

c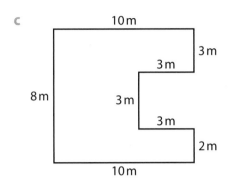

d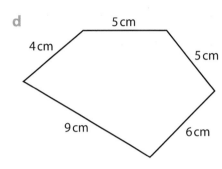

3 Calculate the perimeters of these rectangles.

a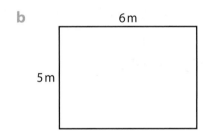

b

c

4 A regular nonagon has nine equal sides.
Each side is 10 cm long.
What is the perimeter of the nonagon?

TASK 3: Finding areas by counting squares

Points to remember

- Area is a measure of the surface covered by a shape.
- Area is measured in square units such as cm² and m².
- Find the area of a shape by counting the squares that it covers.
- Combine part squares to make whole squares.

1. In this diagram all the shapes have the same perimeter.
   Which shape has the largest area? Explain how you know.

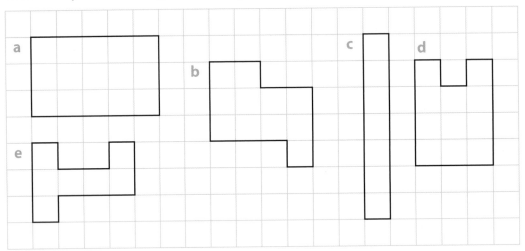

2. This shape is drawn on centimetre squared paper.
   Work out the shaded area.

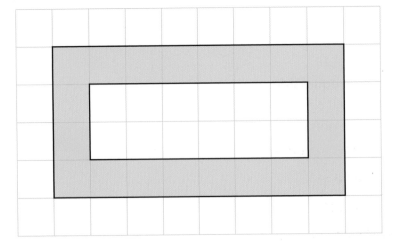

3 This triangle is drawn on centimetre squared paper.
What is the area of the triangle?

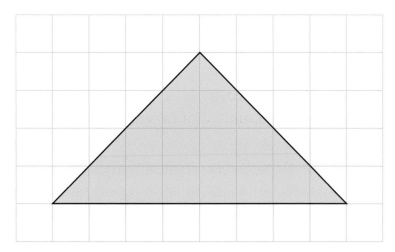

4 Here is part of a plan of a school garden.

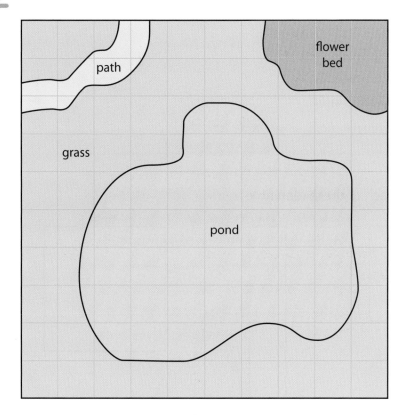

Each square represents 1 square metre.

a Estimate the area of the pond.

b Estimate the area of the path.

c Estimate the area of the flower bed.

d Estimate the area of the grass.

TASK 4: Area of rectangles

Example

Find the area of this rectangle.

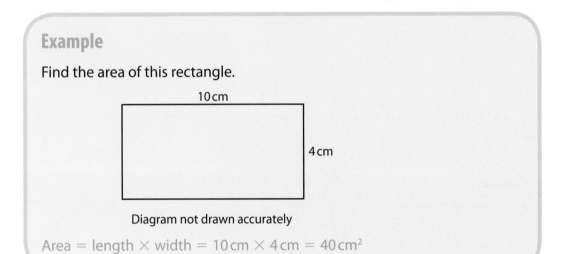

Diagram not drawn accurately

Area = length × width = 10 cm × 4 cm = 40 cm²

1. Work out the area of each of these rectangles.

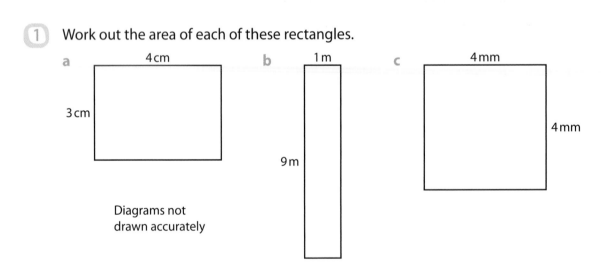

Diagrams not drawn accurately

2. A rectangle is 10 cm long and 3 cm wide.
   What is the area of the rectangle?

3   This shape is made from two rectangles.

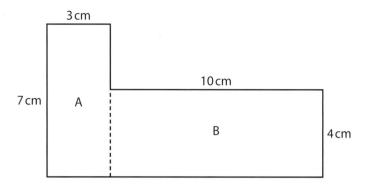

a   What is the area of rectangle A?

b   What is the area of rectangle B?

c   What is the total area of the shape?

4   This shape is a rectangle with a smaller rectangle cut out of it.

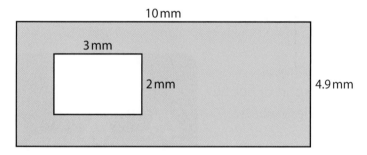

What is the area of the shaded section?

Probability 1

TASK 1: Probability scale

Points to remember

⊙ **Probability** is the likelihood or chance of something happening.

⊙ Words like 'impossible', 'certain', 'likely', 'unlikely' and 'even chance' describe probability.

⊙ Probability can be shown on a probability scale.

| impossible | unlikely | even chance | likely | certain |

1. Think about a sport or hobby you enjoy.
   Write four sentences about your sport or hobby.
   Each sentence must use one of these words:

   certain, likely, unlikely, impossible

   Each word can be used only once.

2. Mark has some bags with some black beads and some white beads.
   He is going to take a bead from each bag without looking.

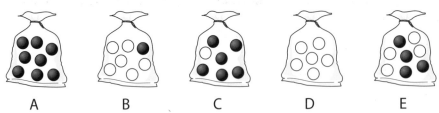

   A   B   C   D   E

   Choose a bag to match each statement.

   a   It is impossible that Mark will take a white bead from the bag.

   b   It is unlikely that Mark will take a white bead from the bag.

   c   There is an even chance that Mark will take a white bead from the bag.

   d   It is likely that Mark will take a white bead from the bag.

   e   It is certain that Mark will take a white bead from the bag.

TASK 2: Probability events

If you roll this dice you can score 1, 2, 3, 4, 5 or 6.

It is **impossible** to get 7.

You are **unlikely** to get a score of less than 2.

You have an **even chance** of getting an odd number score.

You are **likely** to get a score of more than 2.

You are **certain** to get a number less than 10.

1 **a** The spinner has four equal sections: red, yellow, blue and green.

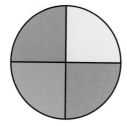 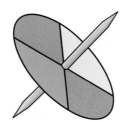

b For each event, write whether it is **likely**, **unlikely**, **even chance**, **certain** or **impossible**.

A The spinner landing on white

B The spinner landing on red

C The spinner landing on a colour

D The spinner landing on red or blue

E The spinner not landing on red

c Copy the probability scale below.
Mark events A, B, C, D and E on it in the right places.

| impossible | unlikely | even chance | likely | certain |

Angles

TASK 1: Amounts of turn

⦿ Points to remember

⊙ The main **compass points** are north (N), east (E), south (S), west (W).

⊙ Angles are measured in **degrees** (°).

⊙ One whole turn is four right angles or 360°.

⊙ One half turn is two right angles or 180°.

⊙ Angles **on a straight line** add up to **180°**.

You will need some squared paper.

① A small robot is programmed to follow instructions and draw a shape.
On squared paper, follow the robot's instructions.
Use a ruler and pencil for your drawing.

Instruction 1: Travel west for 3 squares

Instruction 2: Travel south for 2 squares

Instruction 3: Travel east for 3 squares

Instruction 4: Travel north for 2 squares

What is the name of the shape you have drawn?

2 **a** Megan faces north. She turns a half turn clockwise.
Where is she facing now?

b Mahmood faces south. He turns a quarter turn anticlockwise.
What direction is he facing now?

c Sunetra faces north. She turns clockwise to face south-east.
How many degrees has she turned?

3 Work out the missing angles.

a
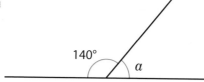
140° *a*

b
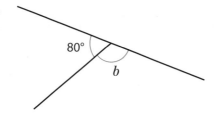
80° *b*

TASK 2: Measuring angles

> ## ⦿ Points to remember
>
> ⦿ Angles can be **acute**, **obtuse** or **reflex**.
>
> ⦿ To measure an angle with a **protractor**:
>   – line up the baseline along one arm
>   of the angle;
>   – put the centre of the baseline where
>   the two arms meet;
>   – count up from 0° on the scale to
>   where the second arm crosses the protractor.

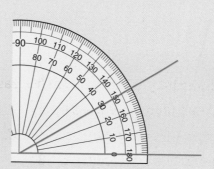

1 Look at these angles.

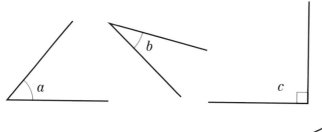

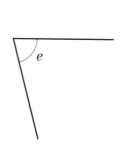

a Write the angles in the order of their size.
Start with the smallest.

b Angle *c* is marked with straight lines.
What does this tell you about the angle?

2 Estimate the size of each acute angle. Record your estimate.
Measure the angle with a protractor and write its actual size.

a

b

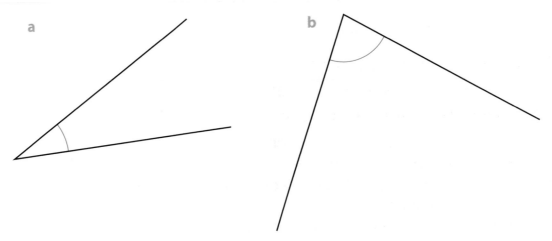

3 Estimate the size of each obtuse angle. Record your estimate.
Measure the angle with a protractor and write its actual size.

a

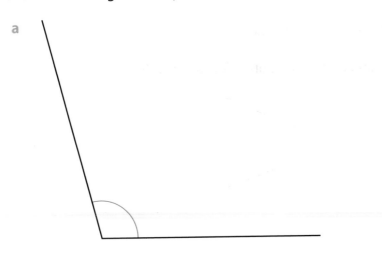

b

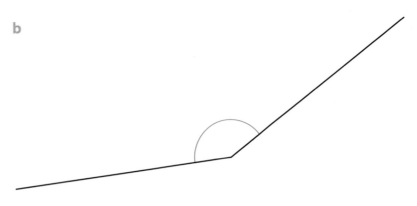

TASK 3: Drawing angles

You will need a ruler, protractor and sharp pencil.

1. Write whether each marked angle is acute or obtuse or reflex.

   a  b 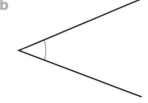 c

2. Draw accurately each of these angles.
   Label the angle with its size.

   a 65° b 125° c 45° d 165°

3. Write all the acute angles in this list.

   34°   134°   91°   184°   345°   9°   201°   89°   179°   1°

TASK 1: Decimals and the number line

Points to remember

⊙ Decimals can be placed on a number line.

⊙ Between any two numbers on a line, there are always more numbers.

1 Write the value of the **9** in each number.

a 3.1**9**   b 7**9**2.3   c 3.**9**   d 8**9**.5

2 What are these numbers?

a Five tenths more than 2.8   b Four tenths less than 7.3

c One hundredth more than 4.9   d Three hundredths less than 6.2

e Two hundredths more than 5.38   f Six hundredths less than 1.04

3 The number 1.5 is halfway between 1.4 and 1.6.

Write the number that is halfway between each pair of numbers.

a 1.1 and 1.7   b 1.2 and 1.3   c 1.6 and 1.7

4 Estimate the numbers that the arrows are pointing to.

TASK 2: Ordering decimals

1. The lengths of some caterpillars are as follows:

   3.6 cm   0.9 cm   4 cm   1.9 cm   0.8 cm

   Write these lengths in order, shortest first.

2. Write each set of numbers in order of size.
   Start with the smallest number each time.

   a 1.76   1.66   1.67

   b 4.66   4   4.6   4.06

   c 69.48   69.4   69.84   69.8

   d 4.96   4.86   4.698   4.98   4.69

   e 0.979   0.97   0.79   0.99   0.799

3. Five athletes took part in the long jump.
   The table on the right shows the results.
   Write the names in order of 1st (the longest jump) to 5th.

Names	Jump (m)
Sharkey	6.4
Singh	6.02
Smart	6.43
Cousins	6.22
Macintyre	6.3

TASK 3: Rounding

Points to remember

- To round a decimal to the nearest whole number, look at the tenths digit. If it is 5 or more, round up. If it is less than 5, round down.
- You can estimate results of calculations by using rounding. For example, 4.8 × 6.2 is about 5 × 6 = 30.

1 The price of a TV set is £438.

   a Is £438 nearer to £400 or to £500?

   b What is the TV's price to the nearest £100?

   c Is £438 nearer to £430 or £440?

   d What is the TV's price to the nearest £10?

2 The price of a washing machine is £485.50.

   a What is its price to the nearest pound?

   b What is its price to the nearest £100?

   c What is its price to the nearest £10?

3 The price of a music player is £174.09.

   a What is its price to the nearest pound?

   b What is its price to the nearest £100?

   c What is its price to the nearest £10?

   d What is its price to the nearest 10p?

4 The price of a car is £12 952.49.

   a What is its price to the nearest pound?

   b What is its price to the nearest £10?

   c What is its price to the nearest £100?

   d What is its price to the nearest £1000?

TASK 4: Decimals and money

Solve these problems **using your calculator**. Remember to show your working.

1. David's return bus fare to work and back is 75p each day.
   He works for 235 days a year.

   a How much are David's bus fares for a year?

   b David could buy a yearly season ticket for his fares for £158.40.
   How much would he save?

2. The total cost for 28 pupils going on a class visit is £204.40.

   a How much is the cost for each pupil?

   b Four teachers are going on the visit. The cost for each teacher is £8.45.
   What is the total cost for the 4 teachers and 28 pupils?

3. Mrs Patel has £8476.32 in the bank.

   a She pays into the bank a cheque for £128.75 and £457.68 in cash.
   How much money does she have in the bank now?

   b Mrs Patel then writes a cheque for £3028.50 for a second-hand car.
   How much money does she have left in the bank?

4. Four friends go to Florida for a holiday.

   They pay a total of £2655.26 for four air tickets and the hotel.

   The cost of the hotel is £956.66.
   What is the cost of each air ticket?

TASK 5: Adding and subtracting decimals

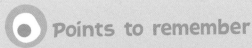

Points to remember

⊙ You can use jottings to help you to do mental calculations.

⊙ To add or subtract decimals in columns, line up the decimal points, put tenths under tenths, and so on.

⊙ Change measurements to the same units before you add or subtract them.

Do these **without using a calculator**.

1. Work these out. Show your working.

   a 6.8 + 3.296 + 15.47

   b 40.7 − 11.84

2. a Robert is 0.9 m tall.
      Alice is 30 cm taller than Robert.
      How tall is Alice in metres?

   b Michelle is 1.25 m tall.
      Sasha is 30 cm shorter than Michelle.
      How tall is Sasha in metres?

   c Write the names of the four children
      in order, shortest first.

3. In a magic square, each row, column and diagonal adds up to the same total.
   Copy and complete these magic squares.
   First work out what the magic total is.

   a

0.6	...	...
...	0.4	...
0.3	...	0.2

   b

2.7	...	...
...	2.1	...
2.1	...	1.5

TASK 6: Using a calculator

 Points to remember

- It is easy to make a mistake when you use a calculator.
  Always estimate the answer and check your answer against the estimate.
- If you make a mistake entering a calculation, clear the display and start again.
- When you use your calculator, write down the calculation that you do.
  It may get you a mark even if you make a mistake.

Use your calculator to answer these questions. Remember to show your working.

1. Copy and complete these calculations by filling in the missing numbers.

   a □ + 784 = 1018   b 618 − □ = 267   c □ × 47 = 1598

2. A shop sells T-shirts and vests.
   T-shirts cost £3.50 each. Vests cost £2.99 each.
   I have £50.

   a How many T-shirts can I buy with £50?

   b How many vests can I buy with £50?

   c I buy two T-shirts and two vests. How much change will I get from £20?

3. The table shows how much it costs to go to a cinema.

	Before 6pm	After 6pm
Adult	£3.45	£5.15
Child (14 or under)	£2.75	£3.75
Senior Citizen (60 or over)	£2.95	£4.90

   Mary (aged 35), her twins (aged 12) and her mother (aged 62) want to go to the cinema.
   They are not sure whether to go before 6:00 pm or after 6:00 pm.
   How much will they save if they go before 6pm?
   Show your working.

Sequences, functions and graphs

TASK 1: Sequences

> **Points to remember**
>
> ⊙ A **sequence** of numbers follows a rule.
> ⊙ If a sequence has equal steps, you can find the rule and the next terms.
> ⊙ You can make a sequence if you know the **first term** and the **rule**.

① Write the next five terms of each of these sequences.

	1st term	Term-to-term rule
a	2	add 10
b	7	add 8
c	105	subtract 5
d	250	subtract 10
e	14	add 8

② Copy and complete each sequence.

a 1, 5, 9, 13, ☐, ☐, 25

b ☐, ☐, 5, 7, 9, 11, ☐

c 3, ☐, ☐, 21, 27, ☐, 39

d 98, 96, ☐, ☐, 90, 88, ☐

e ☐, ☐, 9, ☐, 15, 18, 21

TASK 2: Function machines

Did you know that...?

Claudius Ptolemy was a Greek astronomer and geographer who lived from 85 AD to 165 AD.

He used geometry to show functions.

Points to remember

⊙ A **function machine** has a rule that changes the **input** to the **output**.

⊙ Work through a function machine from the input to the output by following the arrows.

⊙ You can use the labels x for the input and y for the output.

1 Put 6 through each of these one-step function machines.

   a input → | add 12 | → output

   b input → | subtract 4 | → output

   c input → | divide by 3 | → output

   d input → | multiply by 9 | → output

   e input → | add 43 | → output

2 Put 9 through each of these two-step function machines.

   a input → | multiply by 4 | → | add 3 | → output

   b input → | multiply by 8 | → | subtract 7 | → output

   c input → | add 1 | → | multiply by 5 | → output

   d input → | subtract 4 | → | multiply by 6 | → output

   e input → | divide by 3 | → | add 11 | → output

TASK 3: Finding the rule

Points to remember

⊙ If you have only one input and output for a function machine, you can usually find more than one possible rule.

⊙ When you have several inputs and outputs for a function machine, you can find a unique rule.

① Write one operation for each of these one-step function machines.

a 7 → ? → 16

b 11 → ? → 5

c 9 → ? → 22

d 13 → ? → 2

e 8 → ? → 40

② Write two operations for each of these two-step function machines.

a 1 → ? → ? → 7

b 7 → ? → ? → 12

c 3 → ? → ? → 20

d 8 → ? → ? → 50

e 9 → ? → ? → 15

TASK 4: Mapping diagrams

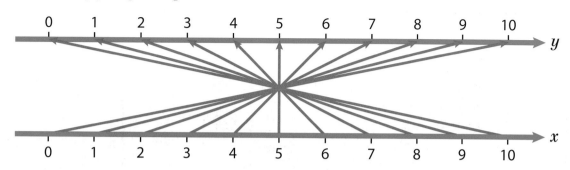

1. Copy and complete the tables for these one-step function machines.

   a input (x) → | add 15 | → output (y)

input (x)	1	5	2	7	9
output (y)					

   b input (x) → | subtract 8 | → output (y)

input (x)	10	17	25	19	36
output (y)					

2. Copy and complete the mapping diagram.

input x	→ multiply by 8 →	output y
1	→	
3	→	
5	→	
6	→	
7	→	

TASK 5: Coordinates

Points to remember

⊙ (3, 4) is a pair of **coordinates**.

⊙ To plot (3, 4) on a grid, start at (0, 0) and go 3 steps to the right and 4 steps up.

⊙ The order of the numbers matters. The point (3, 4) is not the same as the point (4, 3).

You will need squared paper.

1. a ABCD is a square.

    What are the coordinates of point D?

    b The diagonals of the square cross each other at point E.

    What are the coordinates of point E?

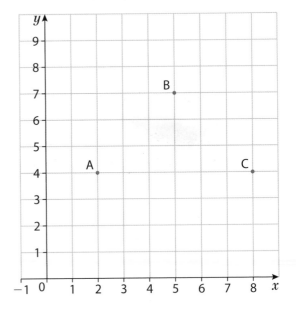

2. Use squared paper to make your own treasure map using coordinate axes.

    Mark six interesting places on your map with a cross.
    Give each of them a name.

    Mark some buried treasure with a small circle.

    Now write a list of the name and coordinates of each of the six interesting places.

    Finally, write the coordinates of the buried treasure.

TASK 6: Graphs

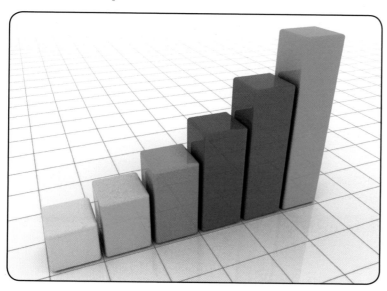

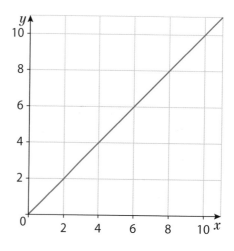

Points to remember

⊙ The input x and the output y of a function machine can be written as (x, y).
⊙ You can plot the (x, y) pairs as coordinate points on a grid.
⊙ The points can be joined to make a graph.

1. Copy and complete the table.

input $(x) \rightarrow$ | add 14 | $\rightarrow$ output (y)

input (x)	1		7		14
output (y)		18		26	
(x, y)					

2. Copy and complete the mapping diagram.

input x	$\rightarrow$	subtract 8	$\rightarrow$	output y	pairs (x, y)
		$\rightarrow$		2	
15		$\rightarrow$			
		$\rightarrow$		14	
29		$\rightarrow$			
		$\rightarrow$		27	

Symmetry and reflection

TASK 1: Reflection

> ### ◉ Points to remember
>
> ⊙ The starting shape is the **object** and the reflected shape is the **image**.
>
> ⊙ In a reflection:
> - the object and image are the same shape and size;
> - matching points on the object and image are the same distance from the **mirror line**;
> - a line joining matching points on the object and image is at right angles to the mirror line.

The baby is looking at himself in the mirror.

His ear and the reflection of his ear are the same distance from the mirror.

The baby is called the **object** and his reflection is called the **image**.

The photograph on the left is of Warkworth Castle in Northumberland.
The castle is reflected in the lake.
The white dotted line is the **mirror line**.
The reflection of the castle is the same shape and size as the actual castle.

You will need some squared paper.

① Copy each diagram carefully on squared paper.
Draw the reflection of the object in the mirror line.

a
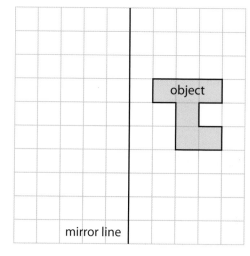

b
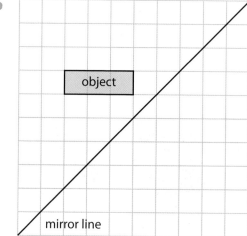

c
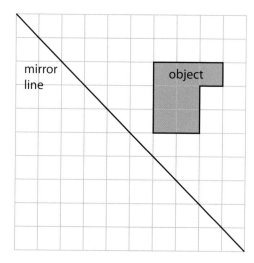

TASK 2: Symmetry

> ## ⊙ Points to remember
>
> - ⊙ A **line of symmetry** or **mirror line** divides a shape into half so that one half folds exactly on top of the other half.
> - ⊙ A regular polygon has the same number of lines of symmetry as sides.

You will need some squared paper.

1. These road signs are from the Highway Code.
   For each road sign, write down how many lines of symmetry there are.

   a Hump
   bridge

   b Low-flying
   aircraft

   c Dual carriage-
   way ends

   d No motor
   vehicles

2. How many lines of symmetry are there in each of these patterns?

   a

   b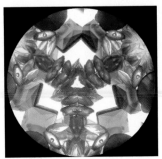

   c

3. Copy the shape on squared paper.

   Shade one more square to make the whole shape symmetrical.

   There are three possible answers.
   Find all of them.

   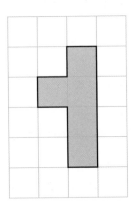

TASK 3: Translation

Points to remember

- When an object is **translated**, every point of the object moves the same distance in the same direction.
- The size and shape of the object and image are identical.

You will need some squared paper.

1. All the shapes in this diagram are translations of the object.
   They have moved up, down, left or right.

   Write the translation for each shape; for example, '3 to the right and 2 up'.
   Remember: start with movements to the right or left before using up or down.

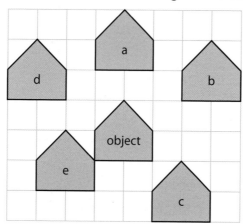

2. Use squared paper.
   Copy this shape in the middle of the page.
   Label the shape 'object'.

   Translate the object:

   a 3 right, 4 up.
      Label the translated shape A.

   b 2 right, 3 down.
      Label the translated shape B.

   c 5 left, 0 up.
      Label the translated shape C.

   d 2 left, 5 up.
      Label the translated shape D.

   e 0 right, 3 down.
      Label the translated shape E.

   f 3 left, 4 down.
      Label the translated shape F.

Decimals and measures

TASK 1: Metres, centimetres and millimetres

Did you know that...?

Since 1971, the UK has used units like **metres**, **kilograms** and **litres**.

These are **metric units**.

The old measures of **miles** and **pints** are still used in places.

These are **imperial units**.

Points to remember

- 4.07 m is 4 metres and 7 centimetres or 407 cm.
- 3.2 m is 3 metres 20 centimetres or 320 cm.
- 2.9 cm is 2 centimetres and 9 millimetres or 29 mm.
- When an answer is a measurement, include the units.

1. Which metric units would you choose to measure these?
   a The length of a biro
   b The distance from London to Glasgow
   c The height of your school
   d The thickness of a pane of glass

2. a Line A is 12.7 cm long. Line B is 48 mm longer than line A.
   How long is line B in centimetres?
   b Line C is 59 mm shorter than line A.
   How long is line C in centimetres?

3. A rectangular pond is 3 metres 28 centimetres long.
   It is 2 metres 57 centimetres wide.
   a What is its perimeter in metres?
   b How much longer is its length than its width?
   Give your answer in centimetres.

TASK 2: Converting units of measurement

 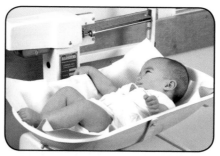 

⊙ Points to remember

- ⊙ Multiplying by 10 moves the digits one place to the left.
  Dividing by 10 moves the digits one place to the right.
  An empty place is filled with 0.
- ⊙ When you multiply or divide by 100, the digits move two places.
- ⊙ When you multiply or divide by 1000, the digits move three places.

1   Which metric units would you choose to measure these?

    a   The weight of newborn baby

    b   The volume of water in a bath

    c   The weight of a tube of sweets

    d   The height of a giraffe

    e   The volume of cola drink in a large bottle

    f   The weight of a packet of biscuits

    g   The capacity of a tea cup

    h   The thickness of a calculator

2   a   What is 65 millimetres in centimetres?   b   What is 4.25 metres in centimetres?

    c   What is 9 metres in millimetres?   d   What is 2000 millimetres in metres?

    e   What is 7.5 kilograms in grams?   f   What is 5000 grams in kilograms?

    g   What is 1.6 litres in millilitres?   h   What is 500 millilitres in litres?

TASK 3: Reading scales

Points to remember

⊙ To read a scale, first decide what each interval represents.

⊙ Work out the values of the marks close to the pointer.

⊙ If the pointer is between two marks, estimate the reading.

① Measure the length of each of these lines to the nearest millimetre.
Write your answer in centimetres.

a ———————————————————

b ———————————————

② Write the readings on these scales. Include the units in your answer.

a

b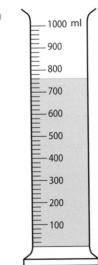

3 Write the readings on these scales. Include the units in your answer.

a
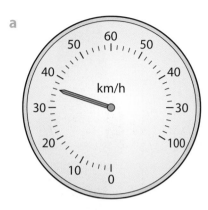

b
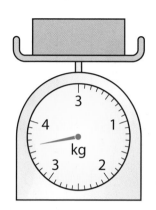

4 There are some apples on the scales.

What is the total weight of the apples?

5 This diagram converts between temperatures in °C and temperatures in °F.

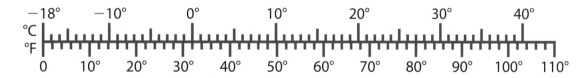

a Estimate the temperature in °C when the temperature is 32 °F.

b Estimate the temperature in °F when the temperature is 25 °C.

c Estimate the temperature in °C when the temperature is 14 °F.

TASK 4: Time

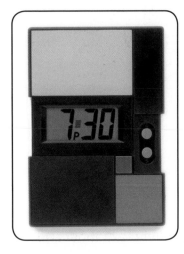  

⊙ Points to remember

⊙ When you write the time, use a colon to separate the hours from the minutes, e.g. 10:15 am.

① How would these be shown on a 12-hour digital clock which shows am or pm?

a Quarter past 7 in the morning

b Twenty-five past 10 in the evening

c Ten to 8 in the morning

d Twenty to 4 in the afternoon

e Five to 12 in the morning

f 19 minutes to 7 in the evening

② a A boat leaves on a trip at 1:20 pm.
The trip takes two and a quarter hours.
At what time does the boat get back?

b Another boat departs at 11:45 am.
It returns at 1:35 pm.
How long is the trip?

③ a A play on the radio is 1 hour 10 minutes long.
It ends at 5:07 pm.
What time did it start?

b A TV programme starts at 8:55 pm.
It finishes at 9:20 pm.
How long is the programme?

c Another programme starts at 11:50 am.
It is 1 hour 15 minutes long.
What time does it finish?

TASK 5: Remainders

1. Work out each division. Give each answer as a mixed number (whole number and fraction).

   a 15 ÷ 2   b 26 ÷ 4   c 32 ÷ 3   d 60 ÷ 8

2. Work out each division. Give each answer as a decimal.

   a 17 ÷ 2   b 43 ÷ 10   c 38 ÷ 4   d 217 ÷ 100

3. Do these **without using your calculator**.

   a Four tins of dog food last 3 days.
      How much dog food is eaten each day?

   b Five friends share 8 pizzas.
      How much pizza does each friend get?

   c Helen and Paul share £75 equally.
      How much does each of them get?

   d Five friends divide the cost of a meal.
      They all pay the same amount.
      The meal cost £34.
      How much does each friend pay?

   e Four cinema tickets cost £23.
      What is the price of each ticket?

TASK 6: Word problems

1   A warehouse stores boxes.

   a   The height of each box is 78 cm.

   What is the height of a pile of 3 boxes?
   Give your answer in metres.

   b   The strip of plastic tape that goes
   round the box is 254 cm long.

   What is the length of two strips of
   tape? Give your answer in metres.

   c   A van can carry 56 boxes.
   Each box holds 48 light bulbs.

   What is the total number of light
   bulbs that the van can carry?

   d   A full box holds 48 light bulbs.

   How many boxes are needed to hold 1250 light bulbs?

2   Which metric units would you choose to measure these?

   a   The length of a garden   b   The weight of a calculator

   c   The amount of petrol in a car's tank   d   The width of a screw

   e   The area of a school's playing field   f   The weight of a pet rabbit

Enquiry 1

TASK 1: Collecting and organising data

> **Points to remember**
> - You can collect data to help find answers to questions.
> - Organising information in a **table** makes it easier to understand.
> - The **frequency** is the number of times an item occurs.

Show these questions to five people. Write a list of the answers for each person.

Questionnaire

1 Which of these things do you like doing in your spare time?
   You may choose **more than one**.

   ☐ Watching television   ☐ Art

   ☐ Playing   ☐ Going out

   ☐ Listening to music   ☐ Reading

   ☐ Going shopping

2 Which of the activities in question 1 is your favourite? ....
   You must choose **one only**.

3 What is your favourite type of television programme? You must choose **one only**.

   ☐ Documentary   ☐ Film

   ☐ Comedy   ☐ News

   ☐ Drama   ☐ Travel

   ☐ Soap   ☐ Sport

   ☐ Quiz   ☐ Reality TV

4 How many times a week do you play sport outside school or work?   ☐

5 How many times a week do you read (excluding work or school)?   ☐

TASK 2: Venn and Carroll diagrams

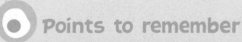

Points to remember

- Venn and Carroll diagrams are sorting diagrams.
- A **Carroll diagram** has rectangles for sorting the data according to whether or not it has the given properties.
- A **Venn diagram** has circles:
  - the data in the overlap of the circles has both properties;
  - the data outside the circles has neither property.

Example

The table shows data on 10 vehicles.

Reference number	Make	Colour	Fuel	Type
1	Ford	Grey	Petrol	Car
2	Ford	White	Diesel	Lorry
3	Volvo	Red	Diesel	Bus
4	Volvo	Silver	Petrol	Car
5	Peugeot	Blue	Diesel	Van
6	Ford	Silver	Petrol	Car
7	Ford	White	Petrol	Car
8	Volvo	Blue	Diesel	Bus
9	Volvo	Blue	Diesel	Car
10	Peugeot	Red	Petrol	Car

This Venn diagram shows this information sorted according to the vehicle being blue and being a car.

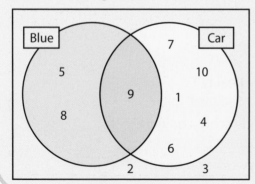

This Carroll diagram shows the data sorted according to the vehicle being a Ford and whether or not it takes diesel.

	Ford	Not Ford
Not diesel fuel	1, 6, 7	4, 10
Diesel fuel	2	3, 5, 8, 9

You sometimes see people in the street who are collecting data for a survey.

Do your own surveys.

1 a Copy and complete the table below left for five people you know.

b Show the information in a Carroll diagram like the one below right.

Name	Number of brothers	Number of sisters

	Has a sister	No sister
Has a brother		
No brother		

2 a Copy and complete the table below left for the same five people.

b Show the information in a Venn diagram like the one below right.

Name	Likes spicy food	Likes fish

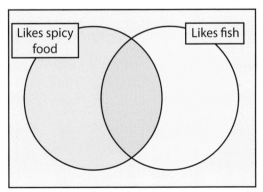

TASK 3: Bar charts and pie charts

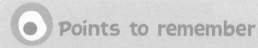

> ## Points to remember
>
> ⊙ In a **bar chart**, the height of a bar shows the frequency for that category.
> ⊙ In a **pie chart**, the size of the 'slice' shows the frequency for that category.

You will need a sharp pencil, ruler and centimetre squared paper.

1 This table shows six of the most popular films in the cinema in the UK during one week in 2007.

   a Draw a bar chart to represent this data.

     Make the scale on the vertical axis go up in 1s.
     Draw the bars 1 cm wide.
     Have a 1 cm gap between bars.

   b Write a sentence to say what the graph shows.

Film	Total ticket sales (£100 000s)
Dreamgirls	13
Blood Diamond	12
The Pursuit of Happyness	8
The Last King of Scotland	4
Casino Royale	3
Miss Potter	3

Data source: uk.imdb.com

2 This pie chart shows the ages of people visiting the cinema in 2005.

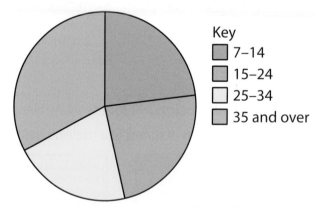

Key
- 7–14
- 15–24
- 25–34
- 35 and over

Data source: www.esrcsocietytoday.ac.uk

   a Which age group made the most visits?

   b Which age group made the fewest visits?

   c Write a sentence about what the pie chart shows.

TASK 4: Bar-line graphs

Points to remember

- A **bar-line graph** shows data where the categories are numbers, such as scores in a game, that can be placed in order.
- The bar-lines must be evenly spaced along the horizontal axis.

Example

The bar-line graph shows the scores Amy got when she rolled a dice 20 times.

The highest score is 6 and the lowest score is 1. The most common score is 6.

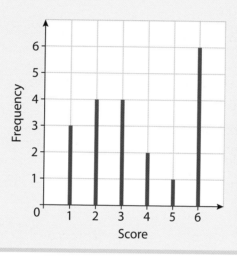

1 The tables show the scores for two classes in a spelling test.

Class 3	
Score	Frequency
4	3
5	2
6	4
7	8
8	7
9	2
10	4

Class 4	
Score	Frequency
4	1
5	2
6	2
7	6
8	10
9	6
10	3

a Draw a bar-line graph for the scores of each class.

b Which class do you think did better in the test? Why?

TASK 5: Mode and range

Example

Simon recorded his spelling test scores every week for a whole term.

His marks were:

6, 8, 10, 10, 9, 8, 8, 9, 10, 8, 6, 9

The dot plot shows his marks in a diagram.

The **mode** for Simon's spelling test scores is 8.

His highest score was 10 and his lowest score was 6, so the **range** was

10 − 6 = 4.

1. Ferdinand has a red dice, a yellow dice and a blue dice. He throws each one 10 times and records the score in a table.

	Frequency		
Score	Red dice	Yellow dice	Blue dice
1	3	2	2
2	1	1	2
3	3	1	3
4	0	3	2
5	3	2	1
6	0	1	0

a Draw a dot plot for each dice.

b Work out the mode and range for each dice.

c Write a sentence comparing the mode and range for the three dice.

Measures

TASK 1: Converting units

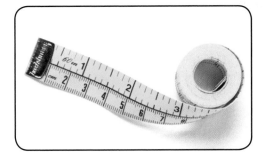

Points to remember

- To change a unit to a *larger* unit in the same system, you **divide**.
- To change a unit to a *smaller* unit, you **multiply**.
- When the answer to a question is a measurement, remember to include the units.

Example 1

Change 567 ml to litres.

567 ml = 0.567 litres

Litres are bigger than millilitres, so divide by 1000.

Example 2

Change 7.8 cm to millimetres.

7.8 cm = 78 mm

Millimetres are smaller than centimetres, so multiply by 10.

1. Write the quantity that is 12 g more than each of these.
   - a 36 g
   - b 490 g
   - c 0.4 kg
   - d 1.02 kg
   - e 0.03 kg

2. Write the quantity that is 35 cm less than each of these.
   - a 50 cm
   - b 120 cm
   - c 362 cm
   - d 0.82 m
   - e 3.6 m

3. Put each set of quantities in order, from smallest to largest.
   - a 1.65 kg   650 g   0.06 kg   0.6 kg
   - b 43 cm   4.3 m   0.4 m   0.03 m   430 cm

TASK 2: Reading scales

Points to remember

- To read a scale, first decide what each interval represents.
- Work out the values of the marks close to the pointer.
- If the pointer lies between two marks, estimate the reading between them.
- When you calculate, make sure the measurements are in the same units.
- Remember to include the units in your answer.

1 Amelia has three parcels.
Two of them are the same and
one is different.

The picture shows the parcels being
weighed, two at a time.

What is the total weight
of all three parcels?
Show your working.

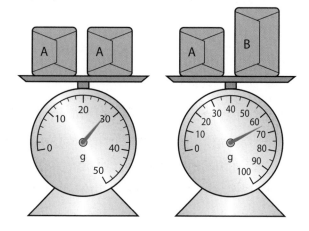

2 Sol's fruit shop sells three different fruit gift baskets.
The biggest basket is twice as heavy as the smallest.

Use the diagram to work out how much the middle size basket weighs.
Show all the steps in your calculations.

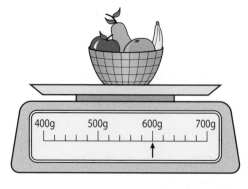

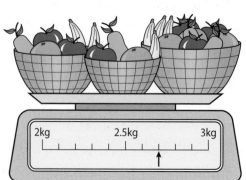

TASK 3: Estimating and measuring

Road sign showing miles

Pint of milk

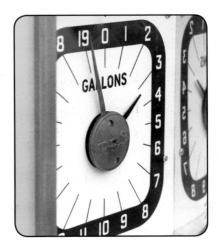

Old petrol pump showing gallons

Points to remember

- ⊙ Metres, kilograms and litres are examples of **metric units**.
- ⊙ Gallons, pints and miles are examples of **imperial units**.
- ⊙ A **pint** is smaller than a litre. It is a bit more than half a litre.
- ⊙ A **mile** is longer than a kilometre. It is roughly 1.5 kilometres.
- ⊙ When the answer is a measurement, remember to include the units.

1 Find three items that have their weight marked on them.
   Examples might be a packet of pasta or a bag of sugar.

   Write down the items and their weights in kilograms or grams.

2 Find three items that hold liquid.
   Examples might be a milk carton, squash bottle or can of soft drink.

   a Write down the item and how much liquid it holds in litres or millilitres.

   b Write down whether each amount of liquid is more or less than a pint.

3 Write down three distances in miles.

   You could look in a road atlas for a mileage table,
   or look at a road sign on the way home from school,
   or ask an adult to tell you the distance to a nearby place.

   a Write down the three distances and how many miles they are.

   b Work out what those distances are, roughly, in kilometres.

TASK 4: Time intervals

Points to remember

- 00:00 is **midnight**. 12:00 is **midday** or **noon**.
- On the 24-hour clock, the hours 00, 01, 02, …, 11 are in the morning; the hours 12, 13, 14, …, 23 are in the afternoon or evening.
- To change 24-hour to 12-hour clock times, subtract 12 from the hours.
- A time line can help with time calculations.

① Make a personal time line.

a Draw a line 24 cm long across the middle of a piece of plain paper.

Mark each centimetre with the hours from 00:00 to 24:00.

```
00:00   01:00   02:00   03:00
|───────|───────|───────|───────|
```

b On the other side of the line, mark the times you do different things on a weekend day.

Write what you do and the time you do it.
For example:
- ⊙ The time you get up
- ⊙ The time you have your breakfast
- ⊙ The time you go out and where you go
and so on.

c Work out how long it takes for you to do the activities on your time line.
For example:
- ⊙ How long do you spend sleeping?
- ⊙ How long do you spend watching TV?
- ⊙ How long do you spend eating your breakfast?
- ⊙ How long do you spend doing homework?
and so on.

TASK 5: Timetables

Points to remember

⊙ Timetables often use the 24-hour clock.

⊙ Each column or row is a separate journey.

⊙ A blank space in a timetable means that there is no stop at that place.

① The Railway Watercress Line is a train service in Hampshire.

This is the timetable for the Railway Watercress Line. It is in 12-hour clock times.

		Steam	Steam	Steam	Steam	Steam	Steam	Steam
SERVICE 2	**ALTON**		10:50	11:55	12:50	1:55	2:50	3:55
	MEDSTEAD		11:04	12:09	1:04	2:09	3:04	4:09
	ROPLEY		11:16	12:21	1:16	2:21	3:16	4:21
	ALRESFORD		11:24	12:29	1:24	2:29	3:24	4:29
	ALRESFORD	11:00	11:43	1:00	1:43	3:00	3:43	
	ROPLEY	11:16	11:56	1:16	1:56	3:16	3:56	
	MEDSTEAD	11:27	12:10	1:27	2:10	3:27	4:10	
	ALTON	11:41	12:24	1:41	2:24	3:41	4:24	

a How many stations are there on the line?

b How long does it take to go from Alton to Alresford?

c Elaine catches the 1.55 train from Alton.
   She gets off at Ropley and goes shopping for 1 hour.
   She catches the next train back from Ropley to Alton.
   At what time does she get back to Alton?

2 Once a month there is a special bus service that links with the Watercress Line trains.

Here is part of the bus timetable.

It is in 12-hour clock times.

Watercress Line train arrives at Alton	11:41	12:24	1:41	2:24	3:41
Alton Station *depart*	11:46	12:29	1:46	2:29	3:46
Alton High Street	11:48	12:31	1:48	2:31	3:48
Chawton	11:58	12:41	1:58	2:41	3:58
Selbourne	12:07	12:50	2:07	2:50	4:07

a Michael is going from Alresford to Alton on the Watercress Line train.
   He will catch the first bus from Alton Station to Selbourne.
   Which train should he catch from Alresford?

b How long is his bus journey from Alton Station to Selbourne?

c Sue catches the 3:00 pm train from Alresford to Alton.
   She then gets the bus to Chawton.
   At what time does she get to Chawton?

d How long does it take Sue to get from Alresford to Chawton?
   Show your working.

Fractions, percentages and direct proportion

TASK 1: Comparing fractions

> ⦿ **Points to remember**
>
> ⊙ To find an **equivalent fraction**, multiply or divide the numerator and the denominator by the same number.
>
> ⊙ Dividing the numerator and the denominator by the same number is **cancelling** or **simplifying** the fraction.
>
> ⊙ Use diagrams to **compare fractions**, or change them into equivalent fractions with the same denominator.

1 Estimate the fraction that the yellow slice is of the whole circle.

a    b    c

2 For each pair of fractions, write the fraction that is bigger.

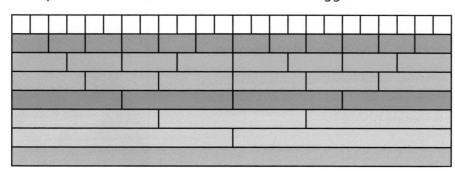

a $\frac{1}{3}$ or $\frac{1}{2}$ b $\frac{1}{6}$ or $\frac{1}{8}$ c $\frac{1}{3}$ or $\frac{3}{8}$ d $\frac{2}{3}$ or $\frac{5}{8}$

e $\frac{2}{3}$ or $\frac{7}{12}$ f $\frac{2}{3}$ or $\frac{3}{4}$ g $\frac{7}{8}$ or $\frac{11}{12}$ h $\frac{1}{6}$ or $\frac{5}{24}$

3 a Write three fractions that are equivalent to $\frac{1}{4}$.

   b Write three fractions that are equivalent to $\frac{2}{3}$.

TASK 2: Fractions, decimals and percentages

Points to remember

- Percentage means 'per hundred', or 'in every hundred'.
- A percentage like 37% can be written as $\frac{37}{100}$ or as 0.37.
- One half is 50%, $\frac{1}{2}$ or 0.5.
- One quarter is 25%, $\frac{1}{4}$ or 0.25.
- One tenth is 10%, $\frac{1}{10}$ or 0.1.
- From this, you can work out that 70% is $\frac{7}{10}$ or 0.7.

1. Change these decimals to percentages.

   a 0.57   b 0.3   c 0.05

2. Change these percentages to decimals.

   a 35%   b 40%   c 2%

3. Change these percentages to fractions.
   Write each fraction in its simplest form.

   a 70%   b 5%   c 25%

4. Change these fractions to percentages.

   a $\frac{7}{10}$ b $\frac{4}{5}$ c $\frac{3}{50}$

5. Solve these problems.

   a In a group of 20 teenagers, 5 of them did
      not have a mobile phone.

      What percentage of the teenagers did not
      have a mobile phone?

   b Mary asked 10 pupils to name their
      favourite sport.
      6 of them said football.

      What percentage of the pupils said football?

   c John did a survey of 100 people.
      36 of them were left-handed.

      What percentage of the people were left-handed?

TASK 3: Percentages of quantities

Points to remember

⊙ To find 10%, divide by 10.

⊙ To find 20%, multiply 10% by 2; to find 30%, multiply 10% by 3, and so on.

⊙ If there is no quick method, first find 1%, then multiply by the percentage.

⊙ Always include any units in the answer.

1 The jug on the right is full of juice.
   It is 100% full.

   How full are the jugs below?
   Give each answer as a percentage.

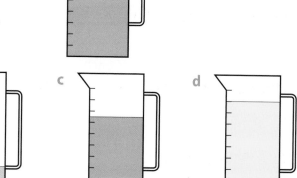

a 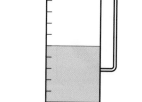   b 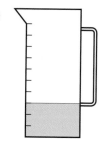   c 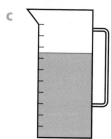   d

2 A shop has 400 greetings cards for sale.

   a 25% of the cards are birthday cards.
      How many cards are birthday cards?

   b 15% of the cards are 'Get well' cards.
      How many cards are 'Get well' cards?

   c 20% of the cards are Mother's Day cards.
      How many cards are Mother's Day cards?

   d 5% of the cards are 'Congratulations' cards.
      How many cards are 'Congratulations' cards?

   e 10% of the cards are Valentine's Day cards.
      How many cards are Valentine's Day cards?

   f The rest of the cards are anniversary cards.
      What percentage of the cards are anniversary cards?

TASK 4: Working with fractions

Points to remember

- You can add or subtract fractions if they have the same denominator.
- To add or subtract fractions with different denominators, change them to fractions with the same denominator.
- Find fractions of numbers by dividing, e.g. to find one third, divide by 3.
- To find three fifths, find one fifth then multiply by 3.

1　Work these out. Draw or imagine a suitable strip of squares to help you.

　　a　$\frac{1}{4} + \frac{1}{12}$ 　　　　　　b　$\frac{5}{12} + \frac{1}{6}$ 　　　　　　c　$\frac{1}{3} - \frac{1}{4}$

2　What fraction of an hour is each of these?

　　a　20 minutes

　　b　45 minutes

　　c　5 minutes

3　What fraction of £1 is each of these?

　　a　10p

　　b　2p

　　c　1p

4　Solve these problems. Show your working.

　　a　A video game costs £120.
　　　　Jason has saved $\frac{3}{4}$ of the cost.
　　　　How much money has he saved?

　　b　A jug of juice contains 400 millilitres.
　　　　Rachel pours $\frac{2}{5}$ of the juice in the jug into some glasses.
　　　　How much juice does Rachel pour out?

　　c　There are 800 pupils in a school.
　　　　$\frac{7}{10}$ of them live 2 miles or less from the school.
　　　　How many pupils live more than 2 miles from the school?

TASK 5: Introducing ratio and proportion

Points to remember

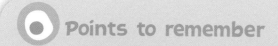

- 2 in every 3 of these beads is blue.
  The **proportion** or **fraction** of blue beads is $\frac{2}{3}$.
- There is 1 red bead for every 2 blue beads.
  The **ratio** of red beads to blue beads is 1:2.
- To simplify a ratio, divide each side by the same number.
  For example, 5:10 is equivalent to 1:2.

1. Two in every three beads on a string are red.

 a. The string of beads continues in the same way.

 Copy and complete this table.

Red beads	Blue beads	Total
2	1	3
4	…	…
16	…	…
…	30	…
…	100	…

 b. If you know the number of red beads, explain how to work out the number of blue beads.

 c. If you know the number of blue beads, explain how to work out the number of red beads.

2. Three in every five beads on a string are red.

 The string of beads continues in the same way.

 Copy and complete this table.

Red beads	Blue beads	Total
…	…	15
…	…	20
…	…	30
…	…	55

TASK 6: Scaling up and down

Points to remember

- In **scaling** problems, think carefully about whether to scale up by multiplying or scale down by dividing.
- It is sometimes useful to write down a statement about one thing.
- Always write down the calculation that you do to show your working.

Here are the ingredients for lemon and mint squash. The ingredients will make 12 drinks when the squash is mixed with extra water.

Lemon and mint squash
50 g mint
60 ml lemon juice
1.5 litres of water
600 g sugar

1. Sam is going to make some squash using 100 g of mint.
   How much lemon juice, water and sugar should he use?

2. How many drinks can be made using 30 ml of lemon juice?

3. How many drinks can be made using 200 g of sugar?

4. How much lemon juice would you need to put with 200 g of mint?

5. The finished drink should be a mixture of $\frac{1}{3}$ squash and $\frac{2}{3}$ extra water.
   Kate puts 150 ml of squash in a glass.
   How much extra water should she put with it?

6. Write the list of ingredients needed to make squash for 60 drinks.

Probability 2

TASK 1: Probability scale

Points to remember

⊙ A probability scale can show how likely or unlikely events are.

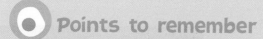

impossible	unlikely	even chance	likely	certain
0		$\frac{1}{2}$		1

You can use numbers to describe probabilities.

For example, Steve has a pet rabbit.

⊙ The probability of Steve's rabbit speaking to him is **0**.

⊙ The probability of Steve needing to clean out his rabbit this week is **1**.

⊙ The chance of Steve's pet rabbit escaping from its hutch when he cleans it out is $\frac{1}{2}$.

① Copy the probability scale.

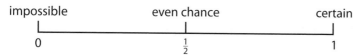

impossible	even chance	certain
0	$\frac{1}{2}$	1

Use arrows to mark the probability of A, B, C, D and E on the scale.

A My pet cat has a female kitten.

B My pet dog will have a litter of 20 puppies.

C My new puppy will chew something.

D Someone in my class has a pet snake.

E I will need to feed my pet dog today.

② Make another copy of the probability scale.
Make up five events of your own.
Mark where they go on the probability scale.

TASK 2: Probability games

Find someone to play two games with.
You will need four coins.

1. Play **Flippers** with a partner.

   Rules

   ⊙ One of you is Heads and one of you is Tails.

   ⊙ Take turns to flip the coin.

   ⊙ If the coin lands heads up, Heads wins a point.
     If the coin lands tails up, Tails wins a point.

   ⊙ The winner is the first to get 5 points.

   Is this a fair game? Explain why.

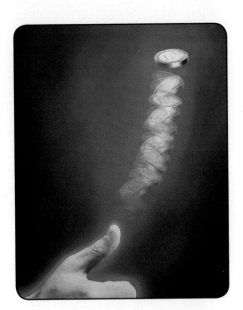

2. Play **Shakers** with a partner.

   Rules

   ⊙ One of you is Heads and one of you is Tails.

   ⊙ Take turns to shake and throw four coins.

   ⊙ For every coin that lands heads up, Heads wins a point.
     For every coin that lands tails up, Tails wins a point.

     For example, if the coins land like this, Heads gets 3 points and Tails gets 1 point.

   ⊙ The winner is the first to get 12 points.
   Is this a fair game? Explain your answer.

TASK 3: Equally likely outcomes

Points to remember

⊙ **Equally likely outcomes** have an equal chance of happening.

⊙ In a **fair game** all the players have an equal chance of winning.

Example

This spinner has four equal sections of different colours.

Mark the probability of getting red on the probability scale.

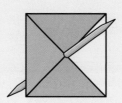

There is 1 chance in 4 of getting red. The probability of red is $\frac{1}{4}$.

impossible	red	even chance	certain
0		$\frac{1}{2}$	1

Here are three different spinners.

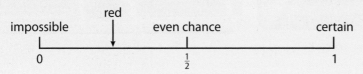

① Copy the probability scale.

impossible	even chance	certain
0	$\frac{1}{2}$	1

Mark on it the probability of getting red with the first spinner.

② Make another copy of the probability scale.

Mark on it the probability of getting red with the second spinner.

③ Make a third copy of the probability scale.

a Mark on it the probability of getting red with the third spinner.

b Now mark on it the probability of getting blue with it.

Properties of shapes

TASK 1: Parallel and perpendicular lines

Points to remember

- **Parallel lines** are always the same distance apart. They never meet.
- **Perpendicular lines** cross at right angles.
- You can use these properties to identify and describe shapes.

You will need some square dotty paper and some coloured pens.

1. The diagram shows a rectangle drawn on dotty paper.

   Pairs of parallel lines have been coloured.
   The right angles are also coloured.

   Draw some more polygons on your dotty paper.

   Draw at least two different triangles and at least five different quadrilaterals.

   Show the parallel sides and right angles on them by using colour.

TASK 2: Properties of shapes

 Points to remember

- You can describe a shape using properties such as:
  - the number of sides, and whether they are the parallel or equal in length;
  - the number of right angles and any equal angles;
  - the number of lines of symmetry.

Rhombus	**Square**	**Rectangle**
Four sides same length	Four sides same length	Two pairs of parallel sides
Two pairs of parallel sides	Two pairs of parallel sides	Four right angles
Opposite angles equal	Four right angles	Opposite sides same length
No lines of symmetry	Four lines of symmetry	Two lines of symmetry
Trapezium	**Equilateral triangle**	**Right-angled triangle**
Four sides	Three sides same length	Three sides
One pair of parallel sides	Three angles same size	One right angle
	Three lines of symmetry	
Regular hexagon		**Irregular pentagon**
Six sides of equal length		Five sides
Six equal angles		
Six lines of symmetry		

You will need some coloured pens or pencils.

1 This pattern is made from two different shapes.
The red and orange tiles are rhombuses.
The yellow, blue and green tiles are right-angled triangles.

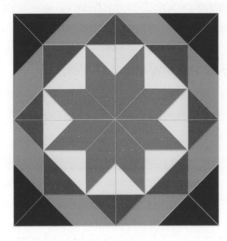

Look for shapes in the pattern.

a What shapes are made from two right-angled triangles?
Write their names. Sketch them and colour them to show how they are made.

b A hexagon is made from two rhombuses and two right-angled triangles.
Sketch and colour the hexagon to show how it is made.

2 This pattern is also made from rhombuses and right-angled triangles.

a Four tiles fit together to make a square.
Sketch and colour the hexagon to show how it is made.

b Three of the tiles fit together to make a pentagon.
Sketch and colour the pentagon to show how it is made.

TASK 3: Classifying shapes

You will need some squared paper.

1. This domino shape is made from two squares joined side to side.

   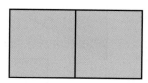

   Draw a domino shape on your squared paper.

   Add another square of the same size so that the three squares are joined side to side.

   How many different shapes can you make from three squares joined side to side? Turning a shape around or flipping it over doesn't count as different.

   Draw the shapes that you make on your squared paper.

2. Now make different shapes from four identical squares joined side to side.

   How many different shapes can you make?

   Draw all your shapes on your squared paper.

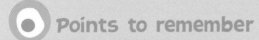

Points to remember

⊙ The **three angles of a triangle** always add up to **180°**.

⊙ If you know two of the angles in a triangle you can calculate the third.

⊙ **Calculate** means to work out without measuring.

1. Here are four triangles drawn on a square grid.

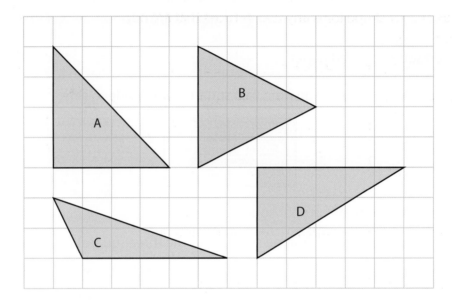

a Which triangle has an obtuse angle?

b Which triangle is isosceles and has a right angle?

c Which triangle is not isosceles but has a right angle?

d Which triangle is isosceles and has three acute angles?

2. What are the sizes of the three angles in triangle A above?
Explain how you know.

3. In triangle B, two of the angles are 70°.
What is the size of the third angle?
Explain how you know.

TASK 5: Drawing 2D shapes on grids

Points to remember

- Use the properties of polygons to:
  - help you to identify them;
  - help you to draw them on a grid.

The corners of 2D shapes are called **vertices**.

A **diagonal** of a 2D shape joins any two vertices that are **not** next to each other.

The diagonals of these shapes are shown by red lines.

You will need square dotty paper, a ruler and a sharp pencil.

① These lines are the diagonals of some shapes.

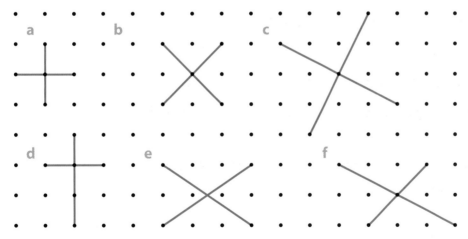

Copy the lines carefully on square dotty paper.
Draw the shapes that have the lines as their diagonals.

For each shape write down its name.

Explain how you know it is that particular shape.

TASK 6: Making shapes and solids

Points to remember

- Solid shapes have edges, faces and vertices.
- You can make new shapes by matching:
  - sides of 2D shapes;
  - faces of identical cubes.

You will need a gummed paper square, a ruler and some scissors.

1. Here is a five-piece tangram.

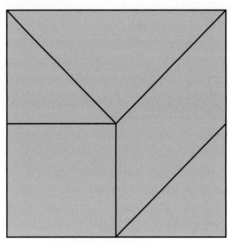

Five-piece tangram

Follow these instructions to make a five-piece tangram from your gummed paper square.

- First find the centre of your square.
  Fold it in half and then in half again.
- Open it out. Use a ruler to mark out a five-piece tangram.
- Cut out the pieces carefully.

Now use the five pieces to make some different shapes.

What shapes can you make? Can you make a hexagon?

Choose one of the shapes you have made.
Stick the pieces in your book to show how to make that shape.

TASK 7: Nets

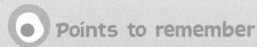

Points to remember

⊙ A **net** is the flat shape that folds up to make a 3D shape.

⊙ When you draw a net, arrange the faces so that they match up when the net is cut out and folded.

1. Choose one of the shapes in the picture above.

   a   Write the name of the shape and its colour.

   b   Draw the net of the shape.

2. Find three boxes or packets at home.
   If possible, they should be different shapes.
   For each packet or box:

   a   Write the number of faces.

   b   Write the number of edges.

   c   Draw its net.

Expressions and equations

TASK 1: Order of operations

Points to remember

⊙ You can change the order of the numbers when you add or multiply, so:

$5 + 3 = 3 + 5$

$4 \times 2 = 2 \times 4$

⊙ You can't change the order when you subtract or divide, so:

$5 - 3 \neq 3 - 5$

$4 \div 2 \neq 2 \div 4$

⊙ Multiply and divide before you add and subtract.

1. Max did these questions for homework.

   Look at each question.
   Did he get it right or wrong?

   a $2 \times 6 + 1 = 13$

   b $8 + 6 \times 3 = 42$

   c $14 - 5 \times 2 = 18$

   d $25 \div 5 + 3 = 8$

   e $32 \div 8 - 1 = 3$

2. Work out the answers for Max.

   a $5 \times 4 + 17$

   b $3 \times 8 - 16$

   c $12 + 4 \times 5$

   d $88 - 6 \times 4$

   e $36 \div 9 + 3$

TASK 2: Using brackets

Did you know that...?

Niccolo Tartaglia was an Italian born around 1500. His father was murdered when Niccolo was 5 years old.

Niccolo's mother was very poor so there was no money pay for him to go to school. He taught himself and became a maths teacher.

He invented the use of round brackets and became famous for solving equations.

He was also the first to use maths to investigate the paths of cannon balls.

Points to remember

⊙ If there are brackets, do what is inside the brackets first.

⊙ If there are no brackets, multiply and divide before you add and subtract.

① Write **True** or **False**.

   a $6 \times (2 + 1) = 18$ b $(19 - 16) \times 5 = 15$ c $4 + 2 \times 6 = 36$

   d $34 - 6 \times 3 = 16$ e $(35 + 7) \div 6 = 7$ f $25 - 15 \div 5 = 2$

② Copy these.
Put brackets where they are needed to make the calculations correct.

   a $9 + 3 \times 7 = 84$ b $8 - 4 \times 7 = 28$

   c $14 + 6 \times 3 = 32$ d $25 - 5 \times 4 = 80$

③ You can use the digits 1, 3 and 5, with $+$, $-$, $\times$ or $\div$, or brackets, to make the number 3.

$$(1 + 5) \div 2 = 3$$

Use the digits 1, 3 and 5, with any of $+$, $-$, $\times$ or $\div$, or brackets, to make these.

   a   16   b   20   c   18

TASK 3: Letters for numbers

 Points to remember

- Letters can represent numbers.
- The expression $n + 5$ tells you to 'add the number 5 to the number n'.
- $6b$ means $6 \times b$.

1. m is the number of days when Cat goes swimming.
   - Hal goes swimming four times as often as Cat.
   - Pat goes swimming six more days than Cat.
   - Chris goes swimming five less days than Cat.
   - Baz goes swimming half as often as Cat.

   Write an expression for:

   a the number of days that Hal goes swimming

   b the number of days that Pat goes swimming

   c the number of days that Chris goes swimming

   d the number of days that Baz goes swimming.

2. Find n.

   a $n + 41 = 96$

   b $n - 22 = 12$

   c $n \times 4 = 24$

   d $n \div 5 = 6$

   e $10n = 250$

   f $200 - n = 10$

TASK 4: Collecting like terms

 1 Simplify:

 a $5p + 4p$

 c $3x + 6x$

 e $4a + 3a + 6a$

 g $8x + 15x + x - 9x$

 b $7b + 8b$

 d $11y - 3y$

 f $10b + 5b - 3b$

 h $8m + 5m + 13m$

2 Simplify:

 a $9 + 5a + 4a$

 c $4y + 3y + 2y + 6z$

 e $8a + 11b + 4a + 2b$

 b $6x + 3x + 5$

 d $5a + 7a - a + 5b + 9b$

 f $12m + 5n + 8m - n$

TASK 5: Substitution

Points to remember

- $2n + 1$ is an **expression**.
  n stands for any number.

- You can **substitute** a number for a letter.
  When $n = 5$, $2n + 1 = 2 \times 5 + 1 = 11$.

- A **formula** shows a relationship.
  The formula for the cost C of n books at £4 each is $C = 4 \times n$.

① Work out the value of $a + 12$ when:

  a $a = 7$

  b $a = 22$

  c $a = 15$

  d $a = 32$

② Work out the value of $8b$ when:

  a $b = 3$

  b $b = 11$

  c $b = 5$

  d $b = 9$

③ Work out the value of $d - 13$ when:

  a $d = 21$

  b $d = 28$

  c $d = 35$

  d $d = 56$

④ Work out the value of $c \div 5$ when:

  a $c = 30$

  b $c = 10$

  c $c = 45$

  d $c = 40$

TASK 6: Inverse operations

Points to remember

⊙ The inverse of + is − and the inverse of − is +.

⊙ The inverse of × is ÷ and the inverse of ÷ is ×.

1 Write the inverse function machine and work out the input for each of these.

    a input → | add 17 | → 45   **b** input → | subtract 19 | → 44

    c input → | multiply by 8 | → 64   **d** input → | divide by 6 | → 9

    e input → | add 14 | → 33   **f** input → | subtract 15 | → 6

2   **a** 542 people went to the theatre.

      325 people went out in the interval.

      How many people were left in the theatre?

  b Ali's family is going on holiday.

     They have travelled 250 miles.
     They have another 173 miles to go.

     How far are they going altogether?

TASK 7: Solving simple equations

 Points to remember

- You can use inverse operations to solve equations.
- The inverse of + is − and the inverse of − is +.
- The inverse of × is ÷ and the inverse of ÷ is ×.

1 Solve these equations.

   a $x + 6 = 10$ b $a − 7 = 4$

   c $5a = 20$ d $m + 6 = 14$

   e $a − 8 = 5$ f $5x = 40$

2 Copy and complete this grid. Fill in the missing numbers.

a	8	9	11
b	6	3	
$a + b$		12	
$2a$			
$3b$			15
$a − b$			

Enquiry 2

TASK 1: Collecting data

Points to remember

⊙ You can use a **tally chart** to collect data.

⊙ This tally chart shows the hair colour of 30 pupils in a class.

Hair colour	Tally	Frequency
Black	IIII	4
Brown	IIIII IIIII	10
Blonde	IIIII	5
Fair	IIIII IIIII II	12
Red	I	1

⊙ Each set of **tally marks** represents a count of five.

⊙ The **frequency** is the total number in a group or category.

1. Choose a page from a book, magazine or newspaper. It doesn't matter which one.
   Copy this tally chart.

Word	Tally	Frequency
a		
and		
but		
is		
for		
of		
on		
to		

Make a tally of the number of times the words appear on the page.

Then complete the frequency column.

TASK 2: Representing data

Example

100 children were asked who they admire. The results are shown in the table and bar chart.

Category	Frequency
Relative	46
Actor/celebrity	27
Sportsperson	20
Coach or club leader	3
Business person	1
Teacher	2
Doctor	1

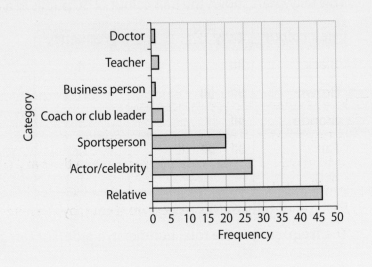

Source: www.censusatschoool.ntu.ac.uk

You will need squared paper, a ruler and a sharp pencil.

1. 26 girls were asked about their favourite activity from a choice of four. The table shows the results.

Activity	Frequency
Sport	7
Seeing friends	9
Computer games	6
Watching TV	4

Draw a bar chart to show the results.

2. 14 boys were asked how they felt about taking part in sport. The table shows the results.

Statement	Frequency
It's good for me	4
It's fun	7
It's hard to do	2
I hate it	1

Draw a bar chart to show the results.

TASK 3: Interpreting data

Points to remember

- A **bar chart** is a way of displaying data.
- It helps to show **patterns** and **features** in the data, such as the largest or smallest group.
- The frequencies of the groups are shown by the heights of the bars.

Example

100 children were asked who they most admire. The results are shown in the bar chart.

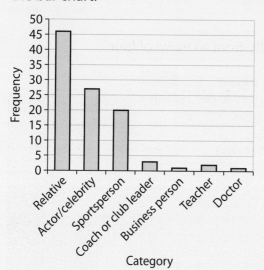

The most common person to admire was a relative.
The least common person to admire was a doctor or business person.

① Look at this bar chart.

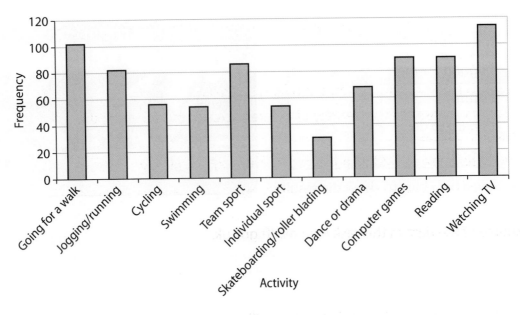

a Write a title for the bar chart.

b Which was the most common activity?

c Which was the least common activity?

d Write two sentences to say what the bar chart shows.

② Look at this bar chart.

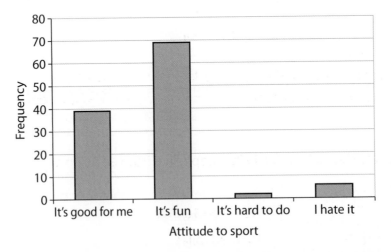

Write two sentences to say what the bar chart shows.

TASK 4: Drawing conclusions

 Points to remember

⊙ Pie charts help to show patterns and features in data.

⊙ You can compare the frequencies of different groups by looking at the sizes of the slices.

⊙ Your **conclusion** should be an answer to the original question.

The source of the data in this task is www.dft.gov.uk.

Example

Question: How far do people travel by train?

1200 people were asked how they use trains.
This pie chart shows the results.

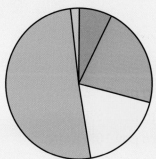

Key

■ Long distances only

■ Short distances only

□ Long and short distances

■ No use

■ Unknown

Conclusion: Just over half of the people asked never use the train.
Just under a quarter use the train for a short distance only.

① This pie chart shows how far 1200 people live from an airport.

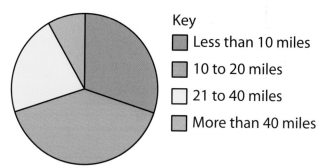

Key

■ Less than 10 miles

■ 10 to 20 miles

□ 21 to 40 miles

■ More than 40 miles

Write two sentences to say what the pie chart tells you.

2 1200 people were asked how many flights they made last year.
The pie chart shows the results.

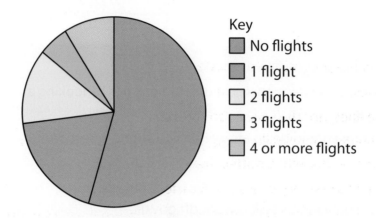

Key
■ No flights
■ 1 flight
□ 2 flights
■ 3 flights
■ 4 or more flights

a Roughly what fraction of the people did not fly?

b Roughly what fraction of the people flew only once?

c Write two sentences to say what the pie chart tells you.

3 1200 people were asked if they were willing to pay more for
air travel to help the environment.
The pie chart shows the results.

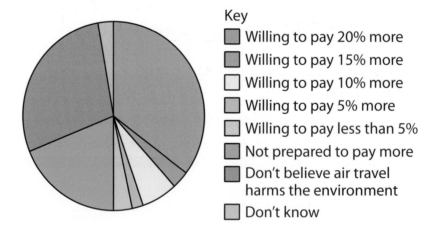

Key
■ Willing to pay 20% more
■ Willing to pay 15% more
□ Willing to pay 10% more
■ Willing to pay 5% more
■ Willing to pay less than 5%
■ Not prepared to pay more
■ Don't believe air travel
  harms the environment
■ Don't know

a Roughly what fraction of people did not believe air travel harms
the environment?

b What was the mode of the answers?

c Roughly what fraction are not prepared to pay anything?

TASK 5: Line graphs

 Points to remember

- A **line graph** has points joined in order.
- Label the axes.
- Number the lines, not the spaces, on the axes.
- If the in-between points make sense, join the points with a solid line. If not, join the points with a dotted line.
- Use the graph to read off values and look for patterns.

You need a piece of squared paper, a ruler and a sharp pencil for this question.

1   A greengrocer charges 60 pence for 1 kilogram of carrots.

    a   Copy and complete the table to show how much carrots cost in pence (p) or pounds (£).

Number of kilograms	1	2	3	4	5	6
Cost (p)						
Cost (£)						

    b   Draw a line graph to show the information in the table. Draw axes like this.

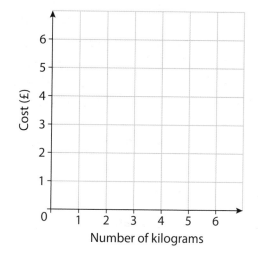

     Join the points on your graph with a line.

    c   Use the graph or the table to work out how much 2.5 kilograms of carrots cost.

    d   How much will 7 kilograms of carrots cost?

TASK 6: More line graphs

 Points to remember

⊙ Line graphs help to show patterns in data.

⊙ Pick out features such as:
  - the highest point and the lowest point;
  - where the graph is going up and where it is going down;
  - any unusual features such as peaks or dips.

Example

Ferdinand plants a bean seed.

He records how tall the bean plant is every day for two weeks.

The table shows his measurements.

Day	1	2	3	4	5	6	7	8	9	10	11	12	13	14
Bean height (cm)	0	0	0	0	1	2	4	8	9	12	14	17	20	24

The graph shows how the bean grew.

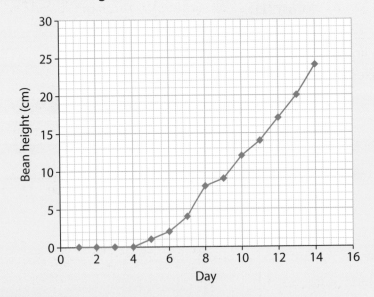

Write down three things about the bean's growth.

The bean started growing on day 4.

It grew steadily bigger and bigger.

After day 4, it grew most between days 7 and 8 and least between days 8 and 9.

1 Two more children grew bean plants and drew graphs to show how well they grew.

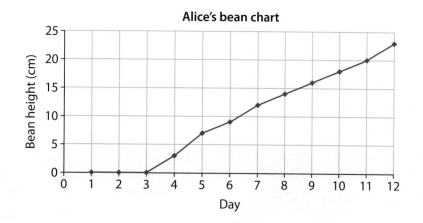

Alice's bean chart

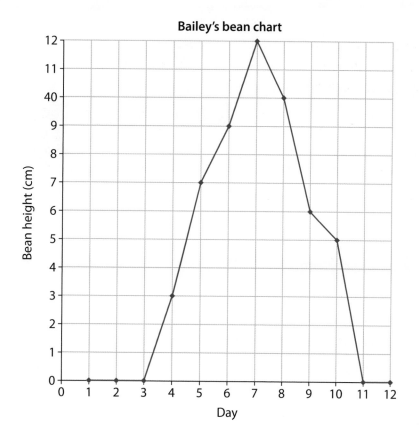

Bailey's bean chart

a Write three things about the growth of Alice and Bailey's beans.

b Which bean grew tallest?

c What do you think happened to Bailey's bean?

Solving number problems

TASK 1: Solving problems with whole numbers

Points to remember

When you are solving problems:

- be systematic;
- look for and make use of patterns;
- keep a careful record of your findings as you go along;
- explain and justify your answers.

1 The number 18 is twice the sum of its digits.

$$18 = 2 \times (1 + 8)$$

The number 27 is three times the sum of its digits.

$$27 = 3 \times (2 + 7)$$

a Which two-digit numbers are four times the sum of their digits?

b Which two-digit numbers are five times, six times, seven times, eight times or nine times the sum of their digits?

c What do the numbers that you have identified all have in common?

TASK 2: Solving problems with number sequences

Points to remember

- Decide whether a sequence is going up or going down.
- Look for patterns in the numbers in a sequence.
- When the difference between one term and the next is always the same, the rule is to add or subtract the difference.

1. Copy and complete these sequences by counting on or back in 9s.

   a 27   36   45   54   ...   .

   b −14   −5   4   13   ...   .

   c 30   21   ...   3   ...   −15   ...

2. Here is a sequence of numbers:

   24   21   18   15   ...

   a What is the rule for this sequence?

   b Copy the sequence and write the next two terms.

   c Work out the 8th term of the sequence.

   d Which term in this sequence is 0?

3. a John has 15 CDs.
      He arranges them in 3 piles.
      Each pile has 2 less CDs than the one before.
      How many CDs are there in each pile?

   b Mira has 24 CDs.
      She arranges them in 4 piles.
      Each pile has 2 more CDs than the one before.
      How many CDs are there in each pile?

TASK 3: Solving problems with decimals

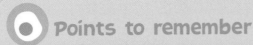

Points to remember

⊙ Use the facts that you know to work out new facts.

⊙ To work out a product such as 4.3 × 6, partition the decimal and multiply each part separately.

⊙ Use jottings to help you if necessary.

1 This is an addition table.
Each number is the sum of the number at the beginning of the row and the number at the top of the column.
For example, 10 is the sum of 6 + 4.

+	3	4
6	9	10
2	5	6

Copy and complete these addition tables.

a

+	0.2	0.9
	0.8	
0.4		

b

+		0.7
0.9	2.2	
		3.1

2 Use all these numbers.

(0.1) (0.2) (0.3) (0.4) (0.5) (0.6)

Copy the triangle.
Write one number in each empty circle.
Do it so that the sum of the numbers along each side of the triangle is 1.

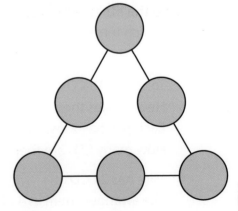

TASK 4: Solving problems with fractions

Points to remember

- You can add and subtract fractions only if they have the same denominator.
- To find a fraction such as $\frac{3}{8}$ of a number, find $\frac{1}{8}$ then multiply by 3.
- Always include any units in the answer.

You can double a fraction by adding it to itself.

For example: $\frac{3}{7} + \frac{3}{7} = \frac{6}{7}$

Sometimes when you double a fraction you can cancel the result.

For example: $\frac{5}{14} + \frac{5}{14} = \frac{10}{14}$ and $\frac{10}{14}$ cancels to $\frac{5}{7}$.

1. There are eleven possible pairs of a fraction and its double on this grid.

$\frac{5}{8}$	$\frac{4}{7}$	$1\frac{1}{3}$	$\frac{5}{16}$	$\frac{3}{5}$
$\frac{3}{4}$	$\frac{3}{16}$	$1\frac{1}{4}$	$\frac{9}{10}$	$\frac{7}{9}$
$\frac{2}{3}$	$\frac{7}{8}$	$1\frac{1}{5}$	$\frac{5}{12}$	$\frac{3}{10}$
$\frac{3}{20}$	$\frac{5}{6}$	$1\frac{1}{2}$	$\frac{1}{3}$	$\frac{3}{8}$

One pair is $\frac{1}{3}$ and $\frac{2}{3}$, because $\frac{2}{3}$ is double $\frac{1}{3}$.

Find the other ten pairs.

Revision unit 1

TASK 1: Measures and measuring scales

Points to remember

- **Kilo** means 1000, **centi** means one hundredth and **milli** means one thousandth.
- To read a scale:
  - decide what each interval represents;
  - work out the numbers for the marks near the pointer;
  - if the pointer lies between marks, estimate the reading.
- If an answer is a measurement, remember to include the units.

(1) *2003 KS2 level 4*

Which value completes each sentence?

a A tea cup is likely to hold about …
   15 ml   150 ml   1500 ml

b A hen's egg is likely to weigh about …
   6 g   60 g   600 g

(2) *Year 7 Optional Test level 4*

What is the mass of this parcel?

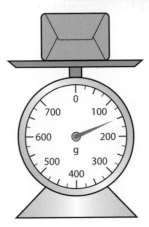

3 *2003 KS2 level 4*

David puts this amount of water in a container.
Then he pours 50 millilitres of the water out.
How much water is left in the container?

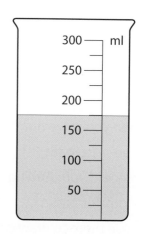

4 *2006 KS2 level 3*

The diagram shows distances on a train journey from Exeter to York.

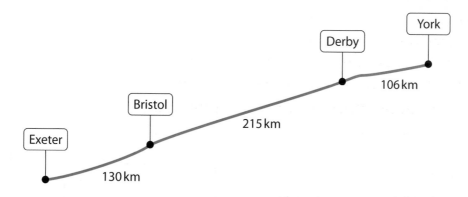

a How many kilometres is it altogether from Exeter to York?

b What is the distance from Derby to York rounded to the nearest 10 km?

5 *2000 KS2 level 4*

Kim has some rectangular tiles.

Each one is 4 centimetres by 9 centimetres.

She makes a design with them.

Calculate the width and height of her design.

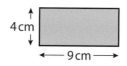

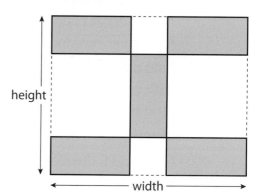

TASK 2: Solving number problems

 Points to remember

When you solve number problems, remember to:

- ◉ be systematic;
- ◉ record your findings as you go along;
- ◉ look for patterns;
- ◉ use them to draw conclusions;
- ◉ explain what you have found out.

Use your calculator when appropriate.

(1) *2006 level 3*

A shop sells birthday cards.
Each card has a code that shows the price.

a Karen pays for two cards.
One card has code A on it.
The other has code C.
Altogether, how much does Karen pay?

b Tariq pays for two cards.
Both cards have code D on them.
Tariq pays with a £10 note.
How much change should he get?

c Greg pays for two cards.
Altogether he pays £3.60.
What could the codes on Greg's cards be?
There are two different answers. Write them both.

Code	Price of card
A	95p
B	£1.25
C	£1.65
D	£1.95
E	£2.35

2 *2003 KS2 level 4*

Parveen has the same number of 20p and 50p coins.
She has £7.00.
How many of each coin has she?

3 *2004 level 4*

I have some 5p coins and some 2p coins.

a I can use some of my coins to make 27p.
Copy and complete the sentences below to show
three different ways to make 27p.

Use .... 5p coins and .... 2p coins.

Use .... 5p coins and .... 2p coins.

Use .... 5p coins and .... 2p coins.

5p coins   2p coins

b I cannot make 27p from 5p coins and 2p coins using an even number of 5p coins.
Explain why not.

4 *2003 KS2 level 4*

These are the prices in a fish and chip shop.

Fish £1.95
Chips   small bag 55p
            large bag 70p
Peas 38p

Luke has £3.
He wants to buy one fish, peas and two
large bags of chips.
How much more money does he need?

TASK 3: Sequences and patterns

⊙ Points to remember

- ⊙ A **sequence** of numbers follows a **rule**.
- ⊙ If a sequence has equal steps, you can work out the rule and the next terms.
- ⊙ A **factor** of a number divides exactly into the number.
  For example, the factors of 6 are 1, 2, 3 and 6.
- ⊙ To plot (4, 5) on a grid, start at (0, 0); go 4 steps to the right and 5 up.

---

1 *1998 KS2 level 3*

Copy this number sequence and fill in the missing numbers.

...   .   34   37   40   ...   .

---

2 *2006 Progress Test level 4*

Jo places equilateral triangles in straight lines to make this sequence.

   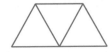 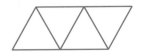

shape number 1   shape number 2   shape number 3   shape number 4

Look at the table on the right.
Jo makes shape number 15.
What is the perimeter of
shape number 15?

Shape number	Perimeter
1	3 cm
2	4 cm
3	5 cm
4	6 cm

---

3 *1996 level 4*

Here is a shaded rectangle.

- **a** What are the coordinates of B?
- **b** M is halfway between D and C.
  What are the coordinates of M?

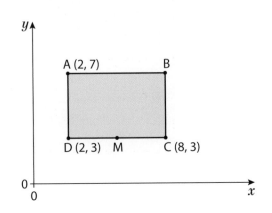

TASK 4: Perimeter and area

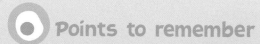

Points to remember

- 1 metre = 100 centimetres and 1 centimetre = 10 millimetres.
- Measure lines from 0 on the ruler.
- **Perimeter** is the total distance around the edge of a shape.
  Perimeter is measured in units of length such as mm, cm or mm.
- Calculate the perimeter by adding all the lengths of the sides.
- **Area** is a measure of the surface that a shape covers.
  Area is measured in square units such as mm^2, cm^2, m^2.
- **Area of a rectangle** = length $\times$ width.

1. Each square on the plan represents 1 square metre.
   Work out the area of the flower bed.

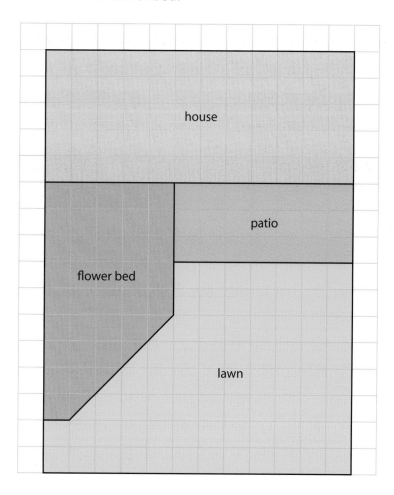

2) Use a ruler to measure the lengths of these lines.

a ───────────────────

b ────

c ──────────────

3) Use a ruler to draw accurately lines of these lengths.
Label each line with its length.

a 4 cm   b 66 mm

4) Calculate the perimeter of these shapes.

a

13 mm

10 mm   10 mm

13 mm

b

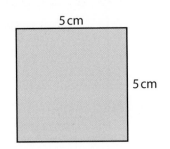

4 cm

2 cm   2.5 cm
              4 cm
1 cm
4 cm   3.5 cm
       7 cm

5) Calculate the area of these rectangles.

a

20 mm

15 mm

b

5 cm

5 cm

TASK 5: Drawing and interpreting graphs and charts

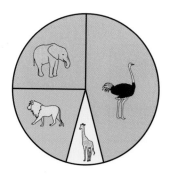

Creatures	Number
Lions	5
Ostriches	11
Giraffes	2
Elephants	6

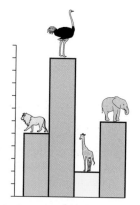

Points to remember

- Graphs, charts and tables are useful for displaying data and making the data easier to interpret.
- Read the scale of a graph carefully.
- Use the key for a pictogram to work out how many each symbol represents.
- Read questions carefully so that you know what you need to find out.

1 *KS2 2001 level 4*

Copy this Venn diagram.

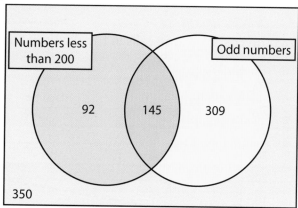

Some numbers are already in place.
Write these numbers in the correct place on the diagram.

99   170   221

2 *KS2 2004 level 4*

Here is a sorting diagram for numbers.

Copy the diagram.

Write a number less than 100 in each space.

	Even	Not even
A square number		
Not a square number		

3 *KS2 1999 level 4*

Five children collect money to plant trees.

Here is a bar chart of the amounts they have raised so far.

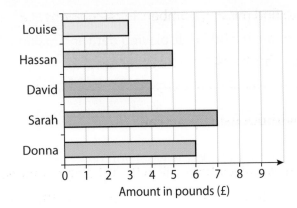

Their target is £40 altogether.

How much more money do they need to reach the target?

4 *KS2 2002 level 4*

This graph shows the cost of phone calls in the daytime and in the evening.

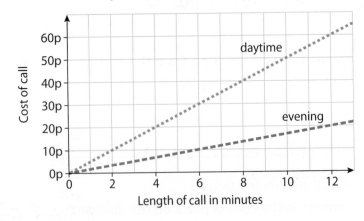

a How much does it cost to make a 9 minute call in the daytime?

b How much more does it cost to make a 6 minute call in the daytime than in the evening?

Revision unit 2

TASK 1: Inverse operations

> **⊙ Points to remember**
>
> - Addition and subtraction are **inverse operations**.
> - Multiplication and division are **inverse operations**.
> - Use inverse operations to find missing numbers in calculations like:
> $18 \times \square = 270$
> - Use inverse operations to check answers to calculations.

Answer questions 1 and 2 **without using your calculator**.

1 *2004 level 3*

Copy and complete these calculations. Fill in the missing numbers.

a $68 + \ldots = 100$ b $20 \times \ldots = 100$ c $300 \div \ldots = 100$ d $65 \times 2 - \ldots = 100$

2 *2004 Progress Test level 4*

Copy and complete these calculations. Fill in the missing numbers.

a $3.7 + 2.5 = \square$ b $2.9 + \square = 4$

For questions 3 and 4 you may **use your calculator**.

3 *2004 Progress Test level 3*

Copy and complete these calculations. Fill in the missing numbers.

a $\ldots + 789 = 1023$ b $718 - \ldots = 367$ c $\ldots \times 57 = 1938$

4 *2003 KS2 level 4*

The three numbers on each line add up to 763.
Write in the missing numbers.

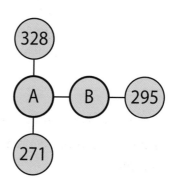

TASK 2: Equivalent fractions, decimals and percentages

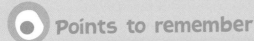

Points to remember

- Change a fraction to a decimal by dividing the numerator by the denominator. You can use a calculator to do this.
- Equivalent fractions, decimals and percentages are represented by the same point on a number line.

① *2003 KS2 level 4*
Choose from these decimals.

0.5   0.8   0.3   0.75   0.4

a Which of the decimals is equivalent to $\frac{1}{2}$?

b Which of the decimals is equivalent to $\frac{3}{4}$?

c Which of the decimals is equivalent to $\frac{4}{5}$?

② Write these decimals as fractions.

a 0.25   b 0.75   c 0.3   d 0.8   e 0.02

③ Write your answers as fractions in their simplest form.

a 25% of the people on the beach are children.
What fraction of the people are children?

b 40% of the fruits in a basket are apples.
What fraction of the fruits are apples?

c 30% of the magazines on a rack are comics.
What fraction of the magazines are comics?

d 15% of the sweets in a jar are toffees.
What fraction of the sweets are toffees?

e 60% of the days in April were sunny.
What fraction of the days in April were sunny?

TASK 3: Expressions and equations

 **Points to remember**

- When there are no brackets, do multiplication and division before addition and subtraction.
- An **expression** is a combination of numbers and letters, such as $8x - 3$.
- You can **substitute** numbers for letters in an expression. For example, when $x = 2$, $8x - 3 = 8 \times 2 - 3 = 13$.
- Use **inverse operations** to find missing numbers in calculations like: $73 + \square = 204$

---

1 *2004 KS2 level 3*

Copy and complete these calculations. Fill in the missing numbers.

a $\square + 85 = 200$ b $4 \times \square = 120$ c $120 - 51 = \square$

2 *2004 level 4*

Work out the values of a, b and c in the number sentences below.

a $3 \times 10 + 4 = a$ b $3 \times 10 + b = 38$ c $c \times 10 + 12 = 52$

3 *1999 KS2 level 4*

Eggs are put in trays of 12.
The trays are packed in boxes.
Each box contains 180 eggs.
How many trays are in each box?

4 a *2006 KS2 Mental Test level 4*

I think of a number, subtract 10 and double the result.
The answer is 44.
What is my number?

b *2006 KS2 Mental Test level 4*

Jenny thought of a number.
She doubled it and then added 4.
The answer was 88.
Which number did she think of?

TASK 4: Symmetry and reflection

Points to remember

⊙ A **line of symmetry** or **mirror line** divides a shape into half so that one half folds exactly on top of the other half.

⊙ The starting shape is the **object**.

⊙ The reflected shape is the **image**.

⊙ Matching points on the object and image are the same distance from the mirror line.

⊙ The line joining matching points on the object and image is at right angles to the mirror line.

You need some squared paper.

① Write down the number of lines of symmetry in each of these car badges.

   a Hyundai   **b** Citroen   **c** Audi

  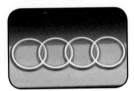

② How many lines of symmetry are there in each shape?

  a A rectangle   **b** A square   **c** A trapezium

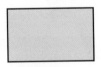 

  d A regular heptagon   **e** An isosceles triangle   **f** A parallelogram

  g A rhombus   **h** A regular hexagon   **i** An equilateral triangle

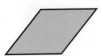

3 *2003 KS2 level 4*

Copy this shape on squared paper.

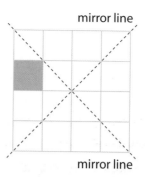

Shade in 3 more squares so that the design is symmetrical in both mirror lines.

4 *2005 KS2 level 4*

Copy this shape on squared paper.
Draw two more lines to make a shape which has a line of symmetry. Use a ruler.

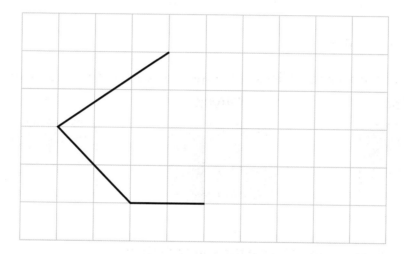

TASK 5: Probability

 Points to remember

- We use numbers to describe the likelihood of events:
  - 0 for **impossible**;
  - 1 for **certain**;
  - $\frac{1}{2}$ for **even chance**.
- A **probability scale** shows how likely or unlikely events are.

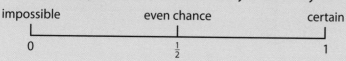

1 *2003 Progress Test level 4*

a Gill puts 4 counters in a bag.
3 counters are blue. 1 counter is white.

Gill is going to take a counter out of the bag without looking.
What is the probability that the counter will be white?
Choose from these fractions.

$$\frac{1}{4} \qquad \frac{1}{3} \qquad \frac{1}{2} \qquad \frac{1}{1}$$

b Sam puts 20 counters in a different bag.
She is going to take a counter out of the bag without looking.
The probability that the counter will be red is $\frac{1}{2}$.
How many red counters are in her bag?

2 *1999 level 4*

Here are four spinners. They are labelled P, Q, R and S.

P 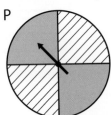 Q 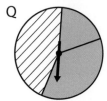 R S

a Which spinner has the greatest chance of the arrow landing on pink?

b Which spinner has the smallest chance of the arrow landing on blue?

c Copy this spinner.
Shade it so that it is certain that the arrow will land on shaded.

d Make another copy of the spinner.
Shade it so that there is a 50% chance that the arrow will
land on shaded.